NORTH AMERICAN GAME FISHES

NORTH AMERICAN
GAME FISHES

BY FRANCESCA LA MONTE
ASSOCIATE CURATOR OF FISHES AT THE
AMERICAN MUSEUM OF NATURAL HISTORY

Illustrations by Janet Roemhild

With a foreword by Philip Wylie

DOUBLEDAY, DORAN AND COMPANY, INC.

GARDEN CITY, NEW YORK 1945

GET A COPY OF THE LOCAL GAME LAWS
BEFORE YOU GO FISHING ANYWHERE

ACKNOWLEDGMENTS

In acknowledging with deep gratitude the willing help that has been given me in preparing this field book, I am in danger of using more space than the body of the book occupies. I think those friends whom I have mentioned here, and many others, must know that all my thanks go to them with this inadequate inclusion of their names in a list. Fortunately, I have had an opportunity to thank most of them personally.

Among my colleagues, I am particularly grateful to Dr. Carl L. Hubbs of the Scripps Institute of Oceanography at La Jolla, California; Dr. Lionel A. Walford of Stanford University; Dr. W. C. Schroeder of the Museum of Comparative Zoology, Cambridge, Massachusetts; Christopher W. Coates of the New York Aquarium; Dr. Arthur W. Henn of the Carnegie Museum, Pittsburgh, Pennsylvania; Cecil Heacox of the State of New York Conservation Department; J. L. Baughman of the Houston, Texas, Museum of Natural History; and Stewart Springer, former Director of Research, Shark Industries, Inc., and to my colleagues here at the American Museum of Natural History—Dr. Roy Chapman Andrews, Dr. William King Gregory, Dr. Charles M. Breder, Mr. John T. Nichols, Dr. Edward M. Weyer, Jr., and Mr. Thomas W. Voter. I have also been most fortunate in having as my artist a former pupil of Dr. Hubbs, Miss Janet Roemhild, whose cheerful and intelligent co-operation cannot be too highly praised.

To the following anglers and angling writers I am indebted for an immense amount of aid: the whole staff of *Field and Stream,* particularly Jack Dunham and Ted Trueblood; Hammond Brown of the OWAA; O. H. P. Rodman; Harvey Kent; the William Schaldachs, senior and junior; Allen Corson; John Alden Knight; G. C. Thomas III; practically the entire town of Louisburg, Nova Scotia; Bob Leckie-Ewing of British Columbia; Verner Bower of Ottawa; and Roy Cann of Yarmouth; also—my sources of information for many years—Erl Roman, Don Stillman, Ray Camp, Al Pflueger, Bill Baxter, Bill Ackerman, and Don McCarthy.

I am indebted to Mr. Eltinge Warner of *Field and Stream* for permission to use the *Field and Stream* fresh-water record chart;

to the International Game Fish Association for the use of their salt-water record chart; to the New York Zoological Society for photographic material for use in the preparation of the plates, and to the editorial and art staffs of Doubleday, Doran for their enthusiastic co-operation, particularly Clara Claasen, Sabra Mallett, and Lee Barker.

This last paragraph is reserved for a few people to whom it is impossible to truly express my gratitude: first, my fellow officers of the International Game Fish Association, Michael Lerner, Van Campen Heilner, Ernest Hemingway, and Philip Wylie. Their help, as always, has been unstinting. Two other anglers have made a most gallant and generous gesture which proves, if proof is needed, the fraternity and good sportsmanship of anglers— L. S. Caine and Kip Farrington have both delayed publication of angling books of their own until mine should be ready!

FRANCESCA LAMONTE

WHAT ANGLER of any considerable experience has not encountered that circumstance, always exciting, frequently disappointing, which he expresses in the words: "I caught it! But what is it?"

What angler, indeed, in the humblest brook or pond, is certain that the adventure will not befall him? And no angler who lets out line in salt water, who then feels a nibble or a strong pull, can guarantee to identify the agent of his quick attention. There are still fishes in the sea man has not captured.

In this book, however, are neatly summarized, surveyed, and described the game fishes of North America's ponds, brooks, rivers, and bordering seas. They are presented non-technically. And that is the estimable virtue of this volume.

Other books have catalogued the fishes of particular regions— but not of all the waters related to this country and in terms suitable for the layman. And most anglers—nearly all—are laymen; even though there is no doubt that ichthyologists fish. So this is everybody's book; everyman's fishing guide.

It has a peculiar additional value, besides its worth as an identification chart of American game fishes. It bestirs the angler's imagination. The California devotee of Yellowtail, after considering these contents, may find himself first musing upon the merits of the Amberjack in Florida and presently undertaking a journey to learn them at first hand. (He better carry this book along; the Amberjack angler will, like as not, catch some other jack or one of the groupers). So here is another function germane to fishing— the promotion of travel, good will, and sportsmanship.

The author of this volume is a lady—a fact which, a generation ago, might have occasioned some surprise. She is also, by profession, an ichthyologist, which would have assured surprise in other days—Associate Curator of Fishes at the American Museum of Natural History in New York City, and Secretary for International Game Fish Association Affairs—a most extensive title for a person of great ability and equal modesty.

Francesca LaMonte is coauthor and translator of several other books on natural history; she speaks several languages and was one of the official representatives from the United States to the

XI International Zoological Congress held in Padua, Italy, in 1930. She is a Fellow of three scientific societies, a member of many others, and is, so far as known, one of only three women ichthyologists in the world.

It is my plain duty to add to this rather staggering list of accomplishments the perhaps more mundane but counterbalancing information that she is also brunette, attractive, and possessed of the sense of humor which is essential among true fishermen.

She has, obviously, fished in many of the streams, lakes, and oceans of the earth. As an ichthyologist, she has accompanied numerous expeditions of the American Museum of Natural History and has added much to the technical knowledge of fish. And, as Secretary of the International Game Fish Association, she has been associated for many years with that group of anglers who are the most exacting sportsmen of all, who will go farthest to examine the weirdest prospects, and who will concern themselves the most meticulously and for the longest time with the least likely brook or mere puddle. In addition to her own direct experience, she has undoubtedly listened to a greater body and variety of expert testimony and anecdote concerning angling than any other woman in the world!

From the foregoing, the reader of this note will gather that, as a journeyman angler myself, I am exceedingly well satisfied with Francesca LaMonte's qualifications for the composition of this book. The identification of fishes is both her business and her recreation. And now that she has chosen to pass on a simplified, understandable version of her lore, every angler is her beneficiary.

Some who con this text and these illustrations may feel that if she has a fault it is in overgenerosity, for she has included here certain fishes which the academician of trout or the burgrave of broadbill might snub as "game." Let no such attitude prevail. Even the lowliest fish here described is considered game in some part of its range and is caught with the greatest of zest. Miss LaMonte has, by including these less spectacular species, ornamented the factor which truly controls the styling of fish as "sporting." It is the spirit of the thing. The lucky inhabitants of Florida or California may be able to pick and choose among several hundred species. But the land-bound resident of the Midwest may have to appoint his "game fish" from a smaller selection. Still, he must have them—and he does. Which is the point.

This book, then, is as complete as high skill can render it and as simple as its subject can be made—wherefore, a book we have never before possessed and one we have always wanted. I heartily commend it to the League of the Wetted Line—the Society of Hook and Sinker—the entire Federation of Fishermen.

PHILIP WYLIE

CONTENTS

INTRODUCTION

This book has a single purpose: to enable anglers to identify their catches.

Anglers must not regard it as an ichthyological textbook. A great many ichthyologically important genera and species will not be found here because they are not game fishes, although many of them are popular and commercially profitable food fishes.

RANGE: The territory covered is from the southern border of the United States to North Latitude 60°. Anglers must note that this excludes Mexico and the West Indies.

GAME FISH: The designation of a fish as "game" is an arbitrary matter. In a narrow sense a game fish is one that can be caught on rod and reel and that, when hooked, puts up enough fight to be sport for the angler. More broadly speaking, it is any fish (caught by angling methods) of which the angler is proud. In parts of our country less populated by the larger and gamier fishes, the source of such pride may be some fish that anglers of more fortunate regions would scorn.

Fishes caught only by one or more of the following methods are not dealt with here: nets, setlines, hand lines, harpoons, spears, any weapon, the hands.

Included are a few fishes that some anglers have protested. Their names were sent in by anglers and the fish-and-game commissions of some states in which they are caught. There are also some omissions for much the same reasons and because of the immense number of local varieties of some fishes, such as the trouts. A non-technical field book of North American trouts, with ample color plates, would be a distinct service to anglers and ichthyologists.

GAME-FISH CHARTS: At the end of the book are the salt-water (I.G.F.A.) and the fresh-water (*Field and Stream*) record rod-and-reel charts. They are limited in scope by the kinds of fishes for which record catches have so far been authenticated.

COMMON NAMES: The American Fisheries Society is making a list of common names of fishes, which they hope will become the standard usage. Unfortunately, it is not yet available. It is time we stopped these immense lists of common names for one fish. Particularly, we should, when possible, discard for other fishes names widely used for one, such as "Bluefish." This is not always possible, of course; for example, "Trout" is so widely used in the south for Weakfish that it would be difficult to change the habit. However, I can see no useful purpose in continuing to list most duplicate names, farfetched names, names used only once in some book, and obviously varied spellings of the same name. It will take time, but this should be straightened out.

SCIENTIFIC NAMES: Most angler-authors now add the scientific name to the common names of fishes. I will not repeat a detailed explanation, available in practically every other book about fishes, of what the scientific name means. It is sufficient to state that it is chosen (and occasionally changed) according to international rules of scientific nomenclature. It can apply to but one fish. The first name is the genus; the second the species (the singular of this word is the same as the plural—species; not specie). Sometimes there is a third scientific name, indicating a subspecies. Proper names following the scientific names are those of the person or persons who first described and gave a scientific name to the fish, in print.

I have often been asked how to pronounce scientific names. This varies with nationality and with methods of teaching Latin. It seems to me unimportant as long as they are pronounced clearly enough so that someone who has other ideas about it can understand what you mean.

IDENTIFICATION: Many fishes cannot be identified offhand, even by competent ichthyologists. Frequently a series of the species, plus a set of complicated measurements and an examination of internal structures, is necessary. Fortunately the identification of most game fishes is not usually so complicated, and quite often local anglers, game wardens, and ichthyologists know very well by sight—as one recognizes a person—a fish whose recognition by a stranger might entail hours of work.

COLOR: This is not a good means of identification in most fishes. It not only changes when the fish is fighting the hook, when it is landed, when it dies, and immediately after death, but it often undergoes rapid and complete changes in life. A grouper that appears red and green one moment may suddenly become white with black spots the next. Most fishes change somewhat with geographic locality, depth, nature of the water, sex, and in the breeding season. The young are almost always quite differently colored from the adult, but we are dealing only with fishes in an adult condition.

SIZE AND MEASUREMENTS: We are dealing here only with anglers' fishes, not with young stages. Anglers could contribute a lot to exact knowledge of fishes if they would take the following measurements of their catches:

Length from tip of snout to where the rays of the tail begin.

Length from tip of snout to a straight line drawn between the upper and lower points of the tail, or to the middle of the outer margin if the tail is straight.

Length of the head, from the tip of the snout to the back margin of the gill cover.

Girth of the fish. Take this in the heaviest part, exclusive of any fin. Use a flexible tape or a piece of string.

Weight of the fish.

The following information is also very useful although more difficult for anglers to obtain and note:

Nature of the teeth; greatest diameter of the eye; how many spines and rays there are in the dorsal and in the anal fins; how many scales there are in a longitudinal row from the back of the gill cover to the base of the tail fin.

Measurements should be taken when the fish is lying on its side, not hanging. In photographing your catch, do not stand in front of, or hold, any of the fins. A photograph taken with the fish lying on its side is of much more use in identification than one of a hanging fish with a rope obscuring the tail, the body distorted by displaced viscera, and the angler proudly grasping one of the fins.

KEYS: The two keys in the back of this book are non-technical and not in the form used by ichthyologists. They apply only to the fishes in the book and are for the sole purpose of enabling the angler to find out to what *group* of fishes his catch belongs. If you know you have caught a snapper you do not need this key. The regular index will guide you to the right pages.

SEASONS, *see* LAWS.

LAWS: Consult the local game warden or the state Fish and Game Commission or Department of Conservation for the laws governing the state *and the district* in which you plan to fish. These laws cover season, size, kinds of fish, and bodies of water. They vary from year to year.

LITERATURE: The standard work on North American fishes is still Jordan and Evermann's *Fishes of North and Middle America,* a heavy, four-volumed, technical work, published in 1896. There is a vast literature on fishes, ranging from huge books to one-page papers, but there is only a minute quantity of non-technical and well-illustrated field books. We need a great many more of these last, particularly regional ones, both for the regions within my limits and bordering regions—in fact, for everywhere in the world. I hope these will be written and that their authors will fill in any gaps I have left.

FRANCESCA LaMONTE

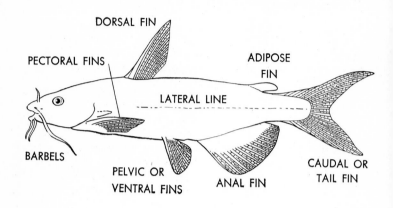

PARTS OF A FISH

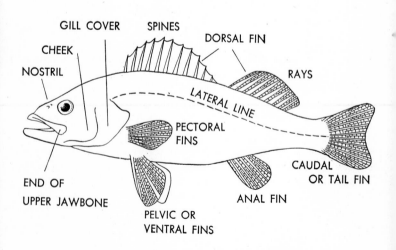

SALT-WATER FISHES

SHARKS

Tiger Shark   *Galeocerdo arcticus* (Faber)

NAMES: Leopard Shark. *Color Plate 1.*

DISTRIBUTION: Atlantic: north to the Gulf of Maine. Pacific: north to Coos Bay, Oregon.

COLOR: See plate. The markings are much plainer in young specimens which are also browner, with distinct large spots.

DISTINGUISHING CHARACTERS: The deeply notched teeth, which are alike in both jaws. The tail pits and tail keels. Upper lobe of the tail is much longer than the lower. The first dorsal fin is opposite the space between the pectoral and ventral fins. A spiracle (pore behind the eye) is present.

SIZE: Up to 14′ long and reported to reach a length of 30′. None of the record catches were made in North American waters.

FOOD: Horseshoe crabs, spiny lobsters, sea turtles, other sharks, tin cans! A goatlike feeder, but eats few of the bony fishes.

HABITS: Caught at the surface in shore waters of warm seas. Its presence is often first discovered during night fishing, when it surfaces more frequently. Never present in numbers.

Thresher Shark   *Alopias vulpinus* (Bonnaterre)

NAMES: Swiveltail, Swingtail, Fox Shark. *Color Plate 1.*

DISTRIBUTION: Atlantic: Florida (infrequent), north to the Gulf of St. Lawrence. Abundant off Block Island, Rhode Island; frequent farther north. Pacific: California to Oregon; most abundant near San Pedro, California.

COLOR: See plate. Sometimes entirely gray.

DISTINGUISHING CHARACTERS: Tail as long as or longer than the rest of body.

SIZE: Up to 20′. The record, a New Zealand specimen, weighed 922 pounds.

FOOD: Mackerel, herring, menhaden, and other smallish schooling fishes.

HABITS: A surface swimmer of temperate seas.

Leopard Shark   *Triakis semifasciata* Girard

NAMES: Cat Shark. *Figure on p. 6.*

DISTRIBUTION: North to San Francisco, California.

COLOR: Gray, lighter below; crossbars running saddle-like across the back and down each side to the mid-line. Uneven dark spots and blotches on the lower sides. The color pattern runs out to the end of the tail.

DISTINGUISHING CHARACTERS: The color pattern.

THRESHER SHARK

TIGER SHARK

PLATE 1

MACKEREL SHARK

PORBEAGLE SHARK

PLATE 2

Size: Three to 5′ or more.

Habits: A common shark south of our range.

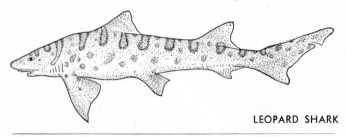

LEOPARD SHARK

THE MACKEREL-SHARK GROUP includes three well-known and easily confused game fishes—the Mackerel Shark, the Porbeagle Shark, and the Man-Eater Shark. They are difficult to tell apart in the water, but when captured are easily distinguishable by their teeth (see detail drawings). As a group, they differ from other sharks chiefly in their nearly symmetrical tails.

There has been the utmost confusion in the common names of these fishes and, in a desire not to add to it, I am omitting all but the most appropriate names.

Side tooth

MAN-EATER   MACKEREL   PORBEAGLE

Mackerel Shark   *Isurus tigris* (Atwood)

Names: Mako, Sharp-nosed Mackerel Shark.

Distribution: North to Cape Cod, Massachusetts.

Color: See *Color Plate 2*.

Distinguishing Characters: Narrowly triangular teeth with smooth edges.

Size: Averages around 5′; runs to over 10′.

Food: Mackerel, herring, and other fishes; squids.

Habits: At surface offshore on calm days. Not very common.

Bonito Shark *Isurus glaucus* (Gill)

NAMES: Mackerel Shark.

DISTRIBUTION: North to Catalina Island, California.

This shark does not differ from the Mackerel Shark of the Atlantic in any easily perceptible way, if at all. It is reported to reach a length of 24′.

Porbeagle Shark *Lamna nasus* (Bonnaterre)

NAMES: Mackerel Shark, Salmon Shark, Bonito Shark.

DISTRIBUTION: Atlantic: New Jersey to Nova Scotia. Pacific: northern California north.

COLOR: See *Color Plate 2*.

DISTINGUISHING CHARACTERS: Teeth with a small cusp at the base on either side of the long, triangular central cusp.

SIZE: Runs to 12′.

FOOD: Mackerel, herring, and other schooling fishes.

HABITS: Surface of high seas on calm days. Apparently the most common of the three Mackerel Sharks, both on Atlantic and Pacific.

Man-Eater Shark *Carcharodon carcharias* (Linnaeus)

NAMES: White Shark. *Color Plate 3*.

DISTRIBUTION: Atlantic: north, occasionally as far as Nova Scotia. Pacific: north to Monterey Bay, California.

COLOR: Usually dark above and lighter below, but occasionally entirely ashen.

DISTINGUISHING CHARACTERS: Rather widely triangular teeth with both edges serrated. (See figure.)

SIZE: Reaches a length of at least 40′.

FOOD: Large fishes such as whiting, weakfish, etc. Sea lions, porpoises, and other miscellaneous items have been reported.

HABITS: A rare, offshore fish.

Hammerhead Shark *Sphyrna zygaena* (Linnaeus)

DISTRIBUTION: Atlantic: Cape Cod, Massachusetts, south. Pacific: Point Conception, California, south. *Color Plate 3*.

COLOR: Gray or brown; lighter below.

DISTINGUISHING CHARACTERS: Hammer-shaped head with eyes at the extremities of the crossbar.

SIZE: Runs to 15′ or more.

FOOD: Spanish mackerel, other sharks, sting rays, other fishes, squids, crustaceans.

HABITS: More common southward. An open-ocean fish, often swimming very near the surface.

MAN-EATER SHARK

HAMMERHEAD SHARK

PLATE 3

PACIFIC MANTA

SAWFISH

PLATE 4

BLACK-TIP SHARKS: Two of the Black-tip Sharks are sometimes caught on rod and reel. As they are generally confused with each other, their distribution is also confused. The most easily distinguishable character for differentiation is the teeth (see figure). The Large Black-tip is said to be the faster fish. The Small Black-tip is the one most frequently taken.

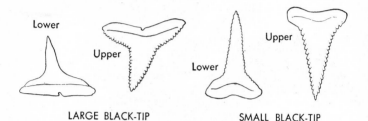

LARGE BLACK-TIP   SMALL BLACK-TIP

Large Black-tip Shark   *Eulamia maculipinnis* (Poey)

Small Black-tip Shark

Eulamia limbatus Müller & Henle

NAMES: Spinner Shark (applies to the Large Black-tip).

DISTRIBUTION: North to Florida, and straggling farther north.

COLOR: Both sharks are gray above, whitish below. Both have black-tipped fins. The black marking is more striking in the Large Black-tip.

DISTINGUISHING CHARACTERS: From other sharks: the black fin tips. From each other: the teeth. Small Black-tip: upper teeth clearly serrated on the edges; lower teeth finely serrated. Large Black-tip: upper teeth microscopically serrated; lower teeth smooth. The first dorsal fin of the Large Black-tip is farther back than that of the Small Black-tip.

SIZE: The Large Black-tip is the larger and slenderer of the two.

FOOD: Fishes.

HABITS: Stewart Springer writes me that the name Spinner Shark "comes from the habit of the shark in jumping or shooting up from the water nearly vertically, falling back with a spectacular splash, and in so doing making about four complete revolutions on its axis. In the spring the spinners are quite common along the east coast of Florida and it is sometimes possible to see fifty in the air at one time. They seem to travel in small schools. . . . Altogether the phenomenon is one of the most exciting things to be seen at sea."

Sawfish   *Pristis pectinatus* Latham

A 736-pound Sawfish caught off Galveston, Texas, and two Florida catches of 600 and 691 pounds have appeared as International Game Fish Association rod-and-reel records. For this reason, this fish, not very generally considered a game fish, is included here.

NAMES: Pez sierra. *Color Plate 4.*

DISTRIBUTION: North to New Jersey. Most common off Florida and in the Gulf of Mexico, ascending the Lower Mississippi River.

COLOR: See *Color Plate 4.*

DISTINGUISHING CHARACTERS: Very heavy, long, wide, flat "saw," extending from upper jaw and bearing large, peglike teeth on either edge. In large specimens this saw runs as wide as 9″ at its base, and the teeth are 2″ long.

SIZE: Said to reach a length of 20′ and a weight of over 1,000 pounds, but specimens of 4′ or so are much more usual.

FOOD: Fishes.

HABITS: Warm seas near sandy shore. Ascends rivers.

THE RAYS

Manta   *Manta birostris* (Walbaum)

NAMES: Devilfish, Blanket Fish. *Color Plate 4.*

There are no rod-and-reel Manta records. It is included here only because of innumerable inquiries concerning its appearance, and that of the Small Devilfish, *Mobula.*

DISTRIBUTION: North to New Jersey in the Atlantic; north to San Diego, California, in the Pacific. A warm-water fish, rare in the northern parts of its ranges.

COLOR: The underside is cream-colored. The Atlantic form lacks white markings on the upper side.

BONY FISHES

Tarpon   *Tarpon atlanticus* (Cuvier & Valenciennes)

NAMES: Tarpum, Silverfish, Grande Ecaille, Sabalo, Savanilla, Silver King, Savalle. *Color Plate 5.*

DISTRIBUTION: North to Nova Scotia; common on both coasts of Florida, off Texas, and as far north as Cape Hatteras, North Carolina. (We again remind anglers of the geographical limits of this book. See page xi.)

COLOR: The body is densely silver with iridescent reflections.

DISTINGUISHING CHARACTERS: Large, thick scales; dorsal fin

BONEFISH

TARPON

PLATE 5

J.R.

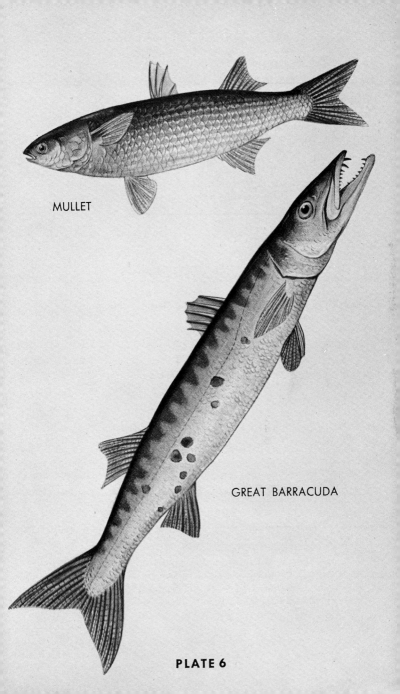

MULLET

GREAT BARRACUDA

PLATE 6

(see plate). A longish, narrow bony plate (the gular plate) on the throat between the branches of the lower jaw.

SIZE: Averages about 60 pounds; reaches over 300 pounds. Smaller Tarpons, generally caught up creeks, are also anglers' fishes.

FOOD: Fishes, particularly mullet and pinfish; crabs.

HABITS: Coastwise and in schools, not far from shore. Comes into fresh water and commonly found in river mouths, bays, and passes. Most active May to September. Present all year round in southern parts of its range.

Ten-Pounder   *Elops saurus* Linnaeus

NAMES: Chiro, John Mariggle, Bonyfish, Big-eyed Herring, Lisa, Lisa Francesca. (The name "Bonefish" for this fish and "Ladyfish" for this and the Bonefish would be better forgotten, as they are the causes of much confusion.)

DISTRIBUTION: Atlantic: north to Cape Cod, Massachusetts; not common north of North Carolina; most common off Florida. The Pacific form, *Elops affinis,* looks like this fish. It does not seem to go north of the Gulf of California, but might straggle within our range.

COLOR: Fins and back blackish-green; rest of body bright silver.

DISTINGUISHING CHARACTERS: The bony plate on the throat, as in the Tarpon. Normal mouth unlike that of the Bonefish. Dorsal fin depressible into a scaly sheath.

SIZE: Reaches 3'; averages less.

FOOD: Crustaceans and smaller fishes.

HABITS: Feeds in open ocean, coming in in schools with the tide. Coastal in rivers and inlets. Present all year in southern Florida.

Bonefish   *Albula vulpes* (Linnaeus)

NAMES: Bananafish, Sanducha, Macabi. (See note under Ten-Pounder.) *Color Plate 5.*

DISTRIBUTION: Atlantic: north to Cape Cod, Massachusetts; most common off Florida Keys. Pacific: occasionally as far north as Monterey Bay, California.

COLOR: The silver sides are strikingly bright. Sometimes there are indistinct dark stripes on the sides.

DISTINGUISHING CHARACTERS: No throat plate. Peculiar pig-like snout overlapping the small, low-set mouth.

SIZE: Averages 2 to 5 pounds; reaches 16 pounds.

FOOD: Crabs and mollusks. A bottom feeder.

HABITS: A warm-sea fish of all year round; plentiful in Florida

14

in the summer months. Schools when small, but is more solitary when larger. Comes in with the tide into very shallow water, mud flats, banks, and sand bars.

Mullet   *Mugil cephalus* Linnaeus

Although sometimes taken on rod and line, this is not a game fish. It is, however, both so frequent a bait and so common a food of Southern game fishes that it is here included for recognition purposes. *Color Plate 6.*

NAMES: Striped Mullet.

DISTRIBUTION: North to Maine; not common north of New York. Present in the Pacific, north to Monterey, California.

COLOR: Usually with a good deal of silver.

DISTINGUISHING CHARACTERS: Shape and color, and a membrane covering part of the eye from each side.

SIZE: Runs larger in the southern parts of its range, reaching 2′, but seldom over 1′ in the North.

FOOD: Feeds in the mud on microscopic organisms.

HABITS: In large schools over mud and in lagoons.

The White Mullet, *Mugil curema* (Blue-back Mullet, Liza, Liza Blanca), runs as large as 3′. It is a southern fish but occasionally straggles to Cape Cod, Massachusetts.

Great Barracuda   *Sphyraena barracuda* (Walbaum)

The barracudas all resemble each other in color and are all pikelike in shape, with long snouts, large mouths, large, uneven teeth, and a projecting lower jaw.

NAMES: Picuda, Becuna, Tiger of the Sea, Sea Tiger, Florida Barracuda, Cuda, Salt-water Muskellunge, Salt-water Pike, Sea Pike. *Color Plate 6.*

DISTRIBUTION: North to South Carolina, straggling as far as Massachusetts. Frequent off Florida.

COLOR: There are apt to be dark spots or blotches on the silvery sides.

DISTINGUISHING CHARACTERS: The fierce array of teeth in the long jaws; the color; the swift movement of the fish, and the long pikelike body.

SIZE: This is the largest of the barracudas. It averages from 5 to 10 pounds and has been known to weigh 100 pounds.

FOOD: Mullet, grunts, and other smaller fishes.

HABITS: Usually solitary, swimming near the surface over outside reefs. Appears to be fearless and approaches with great speed and directness.

MACKEREL

ALBACORE

PLATE 7

COMMON BONITO

OCEANIC BONITO

PLATE 8

Guaguanche

Sphyraena guachancho Cuvier & Valenciennes

NAMES: Guaguanche Pelon.

DISTRIBUTION: North to Pensacola, Florida, and occasionally to Massachusetts. Most frequent off Florida.

COLOR: Olive or yellowish on back; silvery or olive on sides. Some dark dots.

DISTINGUISHING CHARACTERS: Small size; 120 to 130 scales on the lateral line. End of upper jawbone barely reaching a perpendicular from the front of the eye. Reaches a length of 2′ but usually smaller.

Northern Barracuda

Sphyraena borealis DeKay

DISTRIBUTION: Cape Fear, North Carolina, to Cape Cod, Massachusetts.

COLOR: Dark above; silvery below.

DISTINGUISHING CHARACTERS: Its northern range and small size; 115 to 130 scales in the lateral line, and the fact that the end of the upper jawbone does not reach to below the front of the eye.

California Barracuda

Sphyraena argentea Girard

NAMES: Barracouta, Scoots, Scooters.

DISTRIBUTION: North to Puget Sound, Washington, but not usual north of Monterey Bay, California.

COLOR: As in the other barracudas.

DISTINGUISHING CHARACTERS: Its Pacific distribution.

This fish appears in schools; most abundant off California in spring and summer. It reaches a length of over 1′ and a weight of some 12 pounds, but averages smaller.

The Needlefishes

Genera: *Strongylura; Ablennes*

NAMES: Gar, Salt-water Gar, Silver Gar, Billfish, Houndfish, Agujón, Skippick, Sea Pike, Harvest Pike, Longjaws, Timucu.

DISTRIBUTION: There are several species in the Atlantic, running from our southern limit to Maine and including the Gulf of

Mexico; and several in the Pacific, running north to Point Conception, California. They are typically fishes of warm seas.

COLOR: Typically silvery with either green or blue backs. Some of them have bright green bones.

DISTINGUISHING CHARACTERS: Both jaws prolonged into long, thin, fine-toothed and rather fragile beaks; long narrow bodies. They range from a few inches to about 4′ in length.

Although not usually considered game fishes, there are accounts of good fights with these on rod and reel.

Mackerel   *Scomber scombrus* Linnaeus

NAMES: Common Mackerel, Boston Mackerel, Caballa.

DISTRIBUTION: Cape Hatteras, North Carolina, north. Very common.

COLOR: See *Color Plate 7*. Lower part of sides silvery.

DISTINGUISHING CHARACTERS: Finlets following dorsal and anal fins. Pattern of upper body; plain silver color of lower sides. Absence of air bladder. May be confused with the Chub Mackerel, but that fish is mottled on the lower sides, has a much finer-lined pattern above, and also has an air bladder.

SIZE: Average length about 1′; average weight about 1 pound. Has been caught at 7½ pounds and 26″.

FOOD: Smaller fishes, crustaceans.

HABITS: Moves in large schools often mixed with schools of Chub Mackerel. Approaches coasts in spring and goes offshore into deeper water in fall. Frequently taken offshore at the edge of bars. Appears off Hatteras in mid-March and April; off New England in May.

Pacific Mackerel
Pneumatophorus japonicus diego (Ayres)

NAMES: American Mackerel, Greenback Mackerel, Right Mackerel, Striped Mackerel, Zebra Mackerel.

COLOR: Back dark, metallic green. About 10 short, narrow, oblique dark bars on upper sides preceded and followed by irregular short dark marks. Sometimes there are spots between the bars. Sides in general are silvery and iridescent, with a greenish tinge and sometimes dark marks.

DISTINGUISHING CHARACTERS: Finlets. The oblique bars. Body covered with fine scales. A swim bladder. Most easily confused with the Frigate Mackerel.

FOOD: Smaller fishes, squids, shrimps, garbage thrown out from boats.

SIZE: Averages 2 pounds; may reach 3 pounds and length of 1′.

HABITS: Large schools appear irregularly inshore. Usually present in quantity off California from July through November.

Frigate Mackerel   *Auxis thazard* (Lacépède)

NAMES: Mexican Skipjack.

DISTRIBUTION: Atlantic: north to Cape Cod, Massachusetts; more common southward, but never very common. Pacific: north to San Pedro, California.

COLOR: Bluish-green on back and upper sides; sometimes with narrow, dark, oblique stripes extending down as far as the lateral line. Rest of sides iridescent silvery.

DISTINGUISHING CHARACTERS: Finlets following dorsal and anal fins. Scales only on front part of body; larger ones forming a corselet in the region of the pectoral fin.

SIZE: Five pounds, usually less. Said to reach 10.

FOOD: Presumably smaller fishes.

HABITS: Like those of the Mackerel. Very irregular in its appearances.

Albacore   *Germo alalunga* (Gmelin)

NAMES: Long-finned Albacore, Long-finned Tuna, Aliconghi, German, Germon, Abrego. *Color Plate 7.*

DISTRIBUTION: Atlantic: north to Massachusetts, but rare north of Florida. Pacific: Puget Sound to San Diego, California, usually most abundant off California.

DISTINGUISHING CHARACTERS: Finlets following dorsal and anal fins; long pectoral fins reaching to about the third dorsal finlet. Body covered with small scales.

SIZE: Seldom over 50 pounds.

FOOD: Smaller schooling fishes, such as herring, sardines, etc.; plankton, squids.

HABITS: Apparently migratory; erratic in its appearances both as to locality and season. Schools. Offshore near surface. May appear at any time, but usually does so in the warm months.

Common Bonito   *Sarda sarda* (Bloch)

NAMES: Bonito, Blue Bonito, Northern Bonito, Skipjack, Horse Mackerel, Bonejack, Little Tunny, Bloater. *Color Plate 8.*

DISTRIBUTION: North to Cape Cod, Massachusetts, and straggling to Nova Scotia. Cape Ann, Massachusetts, is the northern limit of its regular occurrence. Has been reported abundant off Woods Hole and Martha's Vineyard, Massachusetts, and Block Island, Rhode Island, on the tuna grounds in August and September.

Color: Lower sides are silvery.

Distinguishing Characters: Finlets following dorsal and anal fins. Color pattern: oblique dark bands running forward from ridge of back to just across lateral line. Body entirely scaled. Maxillary extending to below a vertical dropped from the hind margin of the eye. Teeth in jaws larger than those of the Bluefin Tuna, and two or three conspicuously large ones on front of the lower jaw. Note difference (see plate) between the shape and length of the dorsals in this and the Bluefin.

Size: Reaches a weight of 15 pounds and a length of 31″, but averages much less.

Food: Mackerel, menhaden, and other smaller fishes; squids.

Habits: Wanders in schools, usually near the surface, in open sea, but comes inshore in pursuit of its food. Occasionally taken near the bottom.

Oceanic Bonito   *Katsuwonus pelamis* (Linnaeus)

Names: Arctic Bonito, Oceanic Skipjack, Striped Tuna, Skipjack, Watermelon, Victor Fish. *Color Plate 8.*

Distribution: Most common in the trade-wind belts. Atlantic: north to Cape Cod, Massachusetts, but rare as far north. Pacific: north to Point Conception and the Channel Islands, California. Most frequent south of San Diego.

Color: Note that the vertical bars usually present on the back in life disappear immediately after death.

Distinguishing Characters: Finlets following dorsal and anal fins. The horizontal stripes along lower part of body. Absence of scales except for some large ones which form a corselet in the region of the pectoral fin. Short pectoral fin. Small size. No teeth on the roof of the mouth. Lateral line curves downward very suddenly.

Size: This is the smallest of the tunas. It is usually not over 2′ long and does not weigh more than 20 pounds.

Food: Smaller fishes, especially sardines and flying fishes.

Habits: Most common south of our range. Moves around in schools in search of food. An offshore species.

Striped Bonito   *Sarda velox* Meek & Hildebrand

Names: Mexican Bonito.

Distribution: Reported off Block Island, Rhode Island. Out of our range in the Pacific.

Color: Like that of the Oceanic Bonito, but with horizontal stripes on the upper sides.

Distinguishing Characters: Finlets following dorsal and

anal fins. Body entirely covered with scales; maxillary to or nearly to hind margin of eye; horizontal stripes.

SIZE: Reaches 30″ and a weight of about 7 pounds, but usually smaller.

FOOD AND HABITS: Like those of other bonitos.

California Bonito   *Sarda lineolata* (Girard)

DISTRIBUTION: North to Puget Sound, Washington; sometimes abundant near Santa Barbara, California.

COLOR: As in other bonitos; stripes running obliquely from back to, or crossing, the lateral line.

SIZE: Reaches a length of about 30″; usually smaller.

FOOD AND HABITS: Like those of other bonitos.

Bluefin Tuna   *Thunnus thynnus* (Linnaeus)

NAMES: Tuna, Tunny (British), Horse Mackerel, Great Albacore. *Plate 9.*

DISTRIBUTION: Atlantic: north to Hamilton Inlet, Labrador. Rare off Florida. A big run passes Bimini, B.W.I., in late spring or early summer. Present in quantity from approximately July to October from Long Island, New York, north to the Wedgeport–Liverpool district of Nova Scotia; present in some quantity off Newfoundland in warm, dry summers. Concentration areas within our limits are Casco Bay, Maine; Ipswich, Massachusetts; Montauk, New York; Block Island, Rhode Island; and the Wedgeport–Liverpool area, Nova Scotia. Pacific: north to Oregon, not common north of Point Conception, California. Large ones have not been as common in recent years on the famous grounds off Catalina Island, California, as in years past. Season is May to December.

COLOR: The whole fish is iridescent, particularly on the back and cheeks. The top third of the sides and head, across the back, is steel or very dark greenish- or grayish-blue; the rest of the body is grayish-silver. There may be other markings, such as lighter dashes or a broad yellowish or purplish stripe at the lower margin of the blue on the sides. The fins are dusky, with tinges of blue, yellow, or green; the finlets are yellow or yellowish, edged with darker.

DISTINGUISHING CHARACTERS: Finlets following dorsal and anal fins. Pectoral fin much shorter than the head length from the snout to the back of the gill cover. The entire body is scaled. There are small conical teeth in the jaws and fine teeth on the roof of the mouth. Dorsal fins are close to each other. The flesh is pink, sometimes rather grayish.

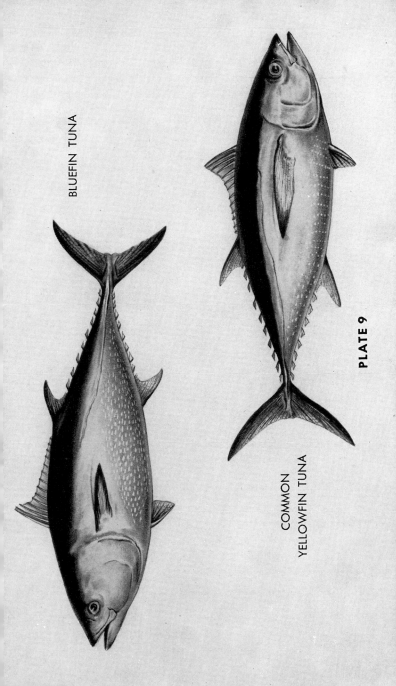

BLUEFIN TUNA

COMMON
YELLOWFIN TUNA

PLATE 9

SIZE: This fish grows to a length of 14' and a weight of 1,800 pounds. Its average weight varies with locality, from 60 or less to 200 or more pounds.

FOOD: Smaller schooling fishes, such as flying fishes, mackerel, herring, menhaden, etc.; squids.

HABITS: Travels in large schools; migratory. Often a very disturbed swimmer, jumping around and thrashing the water. Temperate water, going with currents of warm water to very northern latitudes. Coastal after spawning.

Allison Tuna   *Neothunnus allisoni* (Mowbray)
Yellowfin Tuna   *Neothunnus albacora* (Lowe)
Plate 9
California Yellowfin Tuna
Neothunnus albacora macropterus (Temminck & Schlegel)

The state of our knowledge about the identity of these three fishes is one of the greatest uncertainty. For this reason their distribution cannot be well defined.

DISTRIBUTION: Apparently as follows: Yellowfin Tuna (if separate): Atlantic: north to Maryland. Pacific: north to Point Conception, California.

Allison Tuna (if separate): Atlantic: off Florida, and possibly farther north. Pacific: off California.

COLOR: Much alike in all; no stripes; dark blue on back and upper sides; sometimes a broad yellow band from eye to tail; yellowish fins; lower sides silvery.

DISCUSSION: It would appear quite certain that, if different at all, the California Yellowfin Tuna is just a subspecies of the common Yellowfin Tuna.

In order to determine whether the Yellowfin and the Allison are two fishes or just two stages of one fish, it would be necessary to collect some hundreds of specimens of different sizes of each and to examine them both externally and internally. Dr. Lionel A. Walford has come nearest to doing this, but his specimens were cannery fish, and as he does not mention their sex, we may assume that the viscera had been removed before he saw them. He says, "Among several hundred specimens . . . the dorsal and anal fins were of all lengths, intergrading to such a degree that it was impossible to separate them into two distinct groups. In general the largest had the longest fins. Unless there are some other characters to separate the two . . . it thus looks as if the Allison Tunas of the Pacific coast were merely old specimens of the Yellowfin."

Mr. John T. Nichols and I measured a small amount of material, chiefly photographic (which always means insecurity), and came to the conclusion that at some sizes Yellowfin and Allison are almost exactly alike, but at other sizes specimens of the same size showed very marked differences in the lengths of the dorsal- and anal-fin lobes. Following this idea, we divided the material into three fishes. We, too, had no information as to the sex of the fishes (*Ichth. Contribs. I.G.F.A.* 1941).

I do not know the answer, but I am now inclined to think that: (1) there is only one Yellowfin Tuna (in both Atlantic and Pacific) in our range, and (2) the Yellowfin Tuna and the Allison Tuna are different stages, either growth, or sex, or both, of the same fish.

False Albacore   *Euthynnus alletteratus* (Rafinesque)

NAMES: Little Tunny, Little Tuna, Bonito. *Plate 10.*

DISTRIBUTION: North to Cape Cod, Massachusetts; rather common off New York in summer and fall.

COLOR: Hind part of upper sides with oblique wavy bands and spots; lower sides usually plain silver, but sometimes with a few dark spots below pectoral. General ground colors bluish or greenish above, shading into silvery.

DISTINGUISHING CHARACTERS: Finlets following dorsal and anal fins. The color pattern. Lateral line not curved as in the Oceanic Bonito. Rather large scales in corselet in front near the pectoral fin; the rest of the body without scales.

SIZE: Averages about 10 pounds; may reach 20.

FOOD: Smaller fishes.

HABITS: A pelagic fish of warm seas.

Wahoo *Acanthocybium solandri* (Cuvier & Valenciennes)

NAMES: Peto, Guahu, Guarapucu, Queenfish, Pacific Kingfish, Ocean Barracuda, Ono (Hawaii). *Plate 10.*

DISTRIBUTION: Southern Florida, wandering to Cape Hatteras, North Carolina; fairly frequent about the Florida Keys. Its Pacific distribution is out of our range.

COLOR: Upper sides dark greenish or steel blue, shading into paler silvery, bluish, greenish, or brownish on lower sides. Fins dark. The body sometimes has an overlay of silver which rubs off on one's fingers. Gray or yellowish bars run down from the back, sometimes reaching to the lower margin of the body. These are more distinct in young and in hooked and fighting fishes.

DISTINGUISHING CHARACTERS: Finlets following dorsal and anal fins. Long, low dorsal fin of even height and with about 25 spines (which distinguish it from the Cero, which has only about 15). Large irregular teeth and beaklike upper jaw. Long, cigar-shaped body. The gills form a network, like those of the Swordfish.

SIZE: Averages 15 to 20 pounds but runs much larger. The rod-and-reel record is 133½.

FOOD: Smaller fishes.

HABITS: Open ocean, clear water, or in Gulf Stream and around reefs. Does not school. Never abundant, but winter and spring are its most usual times. Very strong, very swift.

THE SPANISH-MACKEREL GROUP, genus *Scomberomorus*, includes the Cero, Painted Mackerel, Spanish Mackerel, and Sierra Mackerel.

GROUP CHARACTERS: Finlets following dorsal and anal fins. Long, small-scaled body with pointed head, strong jaw teeth, small fine teeth on the roof of the mouth, 15 to 18 dorsal spines, normal gills. Upper part of spiny dorsal dark; lower (near the body), light.

The rayed dorsal fin begins on an imaginary perpendicular dropped to the beginning of the anal fin:

Spots........Painted Mackerel
No spots.....Cero

The rayed dorsal begins in front of an imaginary perpendicular dropped to the beginning of the anal, and the fish is spotted:

Atlantic......Spanish Mackerel
Pacific.......Sierra Mackerel

Cero   *Scomberomorus cavalla* (Cuvier & Valenciennes)

NAMES: Florida Kingfish, Cavalla, Sierra, Kingfish, King Mackerel. *Plate 11.*

DISTRIBUTION: Abundant from Florida to South Carolina; runs north to Cape Cod, Massachusetts.

COLOR: Bright green or blue-green on back and upper sides; iridescent aluminum on rest of body. No spots.

DISTINGUISHING CHARACTERS: Lack of spots. Very slender body. Rayed dorsal fin begins right above the beginning of the anal fin. Lateral line decurves sharply midway down length of the body and proceeds in a straight line to tail.

SIZE: Usually under 15 pounds, but reaches 70 or 80.

FOOD: Fishes, squids.

HABITS: Wanders in large schools; inshore in the Gulf Stream; offshore in winter. Present all the year.

Spanish Mackerel   *Scomberomorus maculatus* Mitchill

NAMES: Cero, Sierra, Spotted Mackerel. *Plate 11.*

DISTRIBUTION: North to Cape Ann, Massachusetts, and fairly

FALSE ALBACORE

WAHOO

PLATE 10

common as far north as New York in summer. Abundant around the Florida Keys and South Carolina.

COLOR: Blue or green on back and upper sides; iridescent silvery below, with orange or bronze spots. Soft dorsal yellowish with dark margin; anal whitish; pectorals black and yellow; tail dark.

DISTINGUISHING CHARACTERS: Spots. Rayed dorsal begins ahead of beginning of anal fin. Lateral line wavy from the point where it decurves to the tail.

SIZE: Reaches 6′ and 20 pounds, but usually nearer 2′.

FOOD: Feeds at surface on smaller fishes and squids.

HABITS: Wanders offshore in large schools, coming inshore in spring before its summer spawning season. Appears in the Gulf off Florida in March, and near New York in July.

Painted Mackerel　　　*Scomberomorus regalis* (Bloch)

NAMES: Sierra, Pintado, Cero, Spotted Cero, Kingfish, Blue-spotted Spanish Mackerel, King Mackerel.

This fish is easily, and very generally, confused with the Spanish Mackerel, from which it differs in the position of the soft (rayed) dorsal fin which begins above the beginning of the anal. There are about 17 dorsal spines. The fish is silvery, with spots, as in the Spanish Mackerel. It also often has a narrow, brownish stripe from the pectoral fin to the caudal.

DISTRIBUTION: North to Cape Cod, Massachusetts. More abundant south of our range, but fairly common around the Florida Keys. It reaches a length of 5′ or 6′ and a weight of 20 pounds, but is usually much smaller.

Sierra Mackerel　　*Scomberomorus sierra* Jordan & Starks

NAMES: Mackerel, Spanish Mackerel, Cero, Sierra, Spotted Mackerel.

DISTRIBUTION: North to Santa Monica, California.

In all other ways like the Spanish Mackerel, and probably is the same fish.

In Monterey Bay, California, there is another fish of this genus, *Scomberomorus concolor* (Lockington), which Walford calls the Monterey Spanish Mackerel. This is rare, but might be confusing if hooked. It is shaped much like a Sierra Mackerel, but the males, according to Walford (1937), are "steel blue on the back, silvery on sides and below, and are without streaks or spots. The females are darker, the silvery part clouded with dark grayish, and have two alternate series of brown spots on the sides."

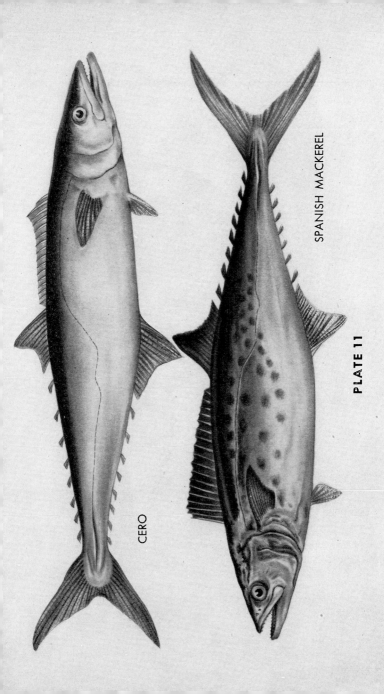

CERO

SPANISH MACKEREL

PLATE 11

THE SPEARED FISHES (*Plate 12*) (Sailfish, Marlin, Spear-fish, Swordfish) are easily recognizable by the prolongation of the upper jaw into a long spear or sword.

Sailfishes differ slightly, according to the ocean they inhabit, but for anglers' purposes we need discuss only two, the Atlantic and the Pacific. There are two varieties of Marlin in the Atlantic and two or more in the Pacific. The Spearfish is a very rare and insufficiently studied fish. There is only one Swordfish.

All of these fishes have a short lower jaw.

No scales; no pelvic fins; heavy flat sword........Swordfish

Scales; pelvic fins; cylindrical spear . . . Sailfish, Spearfish, Marlin.

MARLIN SPEAR

SWORDFISH SWORD

MARLIN SCALE

Atlantic Sailfish
Istiophorus americanus (Cuvier & Valenciennes)

DISTRIBUTION: Common off Florida; straggles to Massachu-setts.

COLOR: Back and upper sides vivid dark blue; rest of body bright silver. Occasionally there are light, lavender-gray lines of dots running from the ridge of the back to across the lateral line. The dorsal fin is vivid, dark purple-blue, sometimes with dark dots. The pelvics are bladelike and black. The tail is blue or black. The anal and pectoral fins are dusky. The spear is very dark.

DISTINGUISHING CHARACTERS: Very high, wide, sail-like dorsal fin. Thornlike scales. Cylindrical, delicate spear. Bladelike pec-toral fins.

SIZE: Averages about 35 pounds with a usual maximum of 60 pounds, but has been taken at 100.

Food: Fishes, such as mullet, etc.

Habits: Frequent in or near the Gulf Stream. Usually schools, but not always. Erratic in occurrence; for example, one large run occurred off Stuart, Florida, in January; another in July.

Pacific Sailfish   *Istiophorus greyi* Jordan & Hill

Distribution: North to Monterey, California, but more common south of our range.

Color: Same color range as that of the Atlantic Sailfish.

Distinguishing Characters: Same as those of the Atlantic Sailfish.

Food: Fishes, such as mackerel, sardines, mullet; squids.

Size: Apparently averages larger than the Atlantic species— about 100 pounds.

Habits: Rare, in summer.

Marlin   Genus: *Makaira*

Only three of the marlins are within the range of this book: the Blue Marlin and the White Marlin of the Atlantic, and the Striped Marlin of the Pacific. The Black Marlin, a very heavy-bodied, rather short-speared fish of the Pacific, does not appear to be within our range.

Blue Marlin   *Makaira nigricans ampla* (Poey)

Names: Cuban Black Marlin.

Distribution: North to Montauk, New York. Within our range it is more common off New York than off Florida, although there are concentration points south of our range.

Color: Back, dorsal fin and upper part of sides bright dark blue; rest of body gleaming silver, sometimes with narrow, light, blue-lavender bands from back toward belly. Other fins purplish-black. While fighting and just after being gaffed, these bands show conspicuously, as do patches of vivid powder blue, especially at the base of the pectoral fins. Eye is bluish or greenish with a dark pupil.

Distinguishing Character: Cylindrical spear; thornlike scales; pelvic fins. The fish is larger and heavier than the White Marlin, with a more sharply pointed and sickle-shaped dorsal-fin lobe.

Size: Averages 200 pounds or more; record, 737 pounds.

Food: Mullet, mackerel, and other fishes.

Habits: In and near the Gulf Stream. Often seen making spectacular leaps from the water. Usually solitary. Most plentiful south of our range in summer.

White Marlin   *Makaira albida* (Poey)

DISTRIBUTION: North to Martha's Vineyard, Massachusetts. Within this range quite frequent off Martha's Vineyard; Montauk and Fire Island, New York; Ocean City, Maryland, and Florida.

COLOR: Bright bluish-green on back and upper sides; usually with narrow, light, lavender-gray bands from ridge of back down over the sides to slightly below the lateral line. Rest of body silver. Dorsal fin brilliant dark blue with dark spots; pelvic fins black; other fins dark greenish. Eye gray-blue with dark pupil rimmed with yellowish.

DISTINGUISHING CHARACTERS: Small delicate build. Dorsal fin lobe rather bluntly rounded and less sharply sickle-shaped than that of the Blue Marlin.

SIZE: Fifty to 100 pounds.

FOOD: Other fishes.

HABITS: Sometimes in numbers; sometimes solitary. One to 25 miles offshore spring and summer; in the warmer months they work north, arriving at Martha's Vineyard around the beginning of July. Offshore waters off Florida from December to June, especially in March.

Striped Marlin   *Makaira mitsukurii* (Jordan & Snyder)

DISTRIBUTION: North to Balboa and Avalon, California. A Pacific form only.

COLOR: Back and upper sides blue-green; rest of body dusky silvery, becoming light, or lavender-gray striped when fighting or leaping. These stripes are about 14 in number and run from the ridge of the back across the body. Dorsal fin deep blue; pelvics black; caudal dark greenish or black; other fins dark grayish or black. Eye appears to be yellowish with a black pupil.

DISTINGUISHING CHARACTERS: Geographical range and general marlin characters. The Black Marlin has a heavier, shorter spear and is heavier through the shoulder.

SIZE: Two hundred and fifty pounds up; 300 to 400 pounds not rare.

FOOD: Fishes, squids.

HABITS: Open ocean; solitary; sometimes quite close to shore. Can be seen leaping from the water even when not hooked. Sometimes occurs in numbers, sometimes in pairs (breeding), and sometimes solitary. June to November. Most famous fishing grounds are off Tocopilla, Chile.

Spearfish   *Tetrapterus belone* Rafinesque

Too few of these fishes have been taken for much to be known about them.

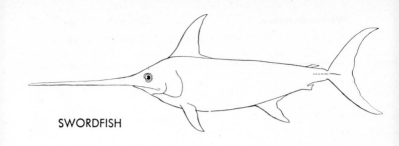

SWORDFISH

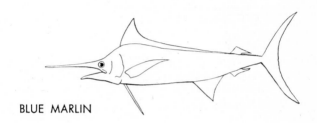

BLUE MARLIN

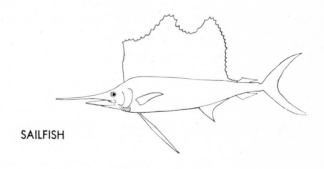

SAILFISH

PLATE 12

DISTRIBUTION: Has been taken off Florida, North Carolina, and in the Pacific out of our range (Hawaii).

COLOR: Much the same as that of the White Marlin except that the stripes from back toward the belly are said to be bluish-green.

DISTINGUISHING CHARACTERS: Scales and pelvic fins present. Spear not as much longer than the lower jaw as in the other speared fishes. A very slender fish with a moderately high dorsal fin which is very long and almost the same height throughout its length.

SIZE: One specimen measured 6' and weighed 60 pounds.

Swordfish   *Xiphias gladius* Linnaeus

NAMES: Broadbill, Broadbill Swordfish.

DISTRIBUTION: Atlantic: north to west coast of Newfoundland; reported off Labrador. Pacific: north to Santa Cruz Island, California.

COLOR: Bronze with a silvery gleam, or brownish black with a rather dirty-white belly. The 3½"-diameter eye is brilliantly blue.

DISTINGUISHING CHARACTERS: No scales in sizes over 4½' long; no pelvics; broad, flat sword.

SIZE: In our range, averages 250 pounds up; 400-pound specimens not rare. Said to reach well over 1,000 pounds.

FOOD: Mackerel, herring, and other schooling fishes; squids.

HABITS: Solitary except on breeding grounds; suns at surface. Distance offshore depends on season, growth stage, and sexual condition. When at surface these fishes do not seem to heed an approaching boat for some time; when they do, they sound. In the South the run begins April and May; Montauk, New York, June to September; Nova Scotia, July to September. In the Pacific, most abundant September to December. Within our range the centers are Montauk, N .Y.; Block Island, R. I., and Cape Breton, Nova Scotia.

THE JACKS (Genus *Caranx*) form a group which contains a number of rather similar fishes, some of which are too rare to be considered game fish. Most of the Pacific jacks are south of our range. The group is characterized by bony scutes or shields on the hind end of the lateral line. There are small teeth in the jaws and on the roof of the mouth.

Blue Runner   *Caranx crysos* (Mitchill)

NAMES: Hardtailed Jack, Jack, Yellowjack, Hardtail, Runner, Yellow Mackerel, Crevalle, Crevalle Jack. *Plate 13.*

DISTRIBUTION: North to Cape Cod, Massachusetts, occasionally straggling to Nova Scotia. Concentration is southward.

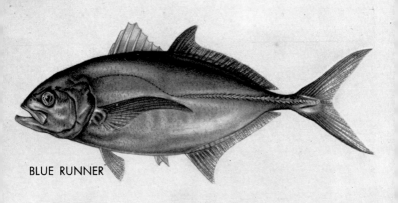

BLUE RUNNER

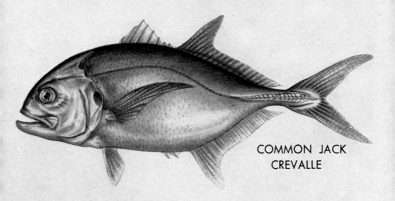

COMMON JACK
CREVALLE

RAINBOW RUNNER

PLATE 13

COLOR: Greenish on back and upper sides, shading into yellow-ish-silvery below. Fins almost colorless. No dark blotch on pec-torals.

DISTINGUISHING CHARACTERS: Breast covered with small scales; 23 to 25 rays in the dorsal fin and 19 to 20 in the anal. No (or very small) spot on the gill cover. No canine teeth on front of the lower jaw. Long, curved pectorals.

SIZE: Averages about 1½ or 2 pounds, but has been taken up to 6.

FOOD: Smaller fishes, such as sardines, mullet, etc.; shrimps, crabs.

HABITS: Schools around reefs and rocks.

Common Jack Crevalle   *Caranx hippos* (Linnaeus)

NAMES: Crevalle, Horse Crevalle, Cavalla Jack, Yellow Caranx, Yellow Mackerel, Tourist Tarpon. *Plate 13.*

DISTRIBUTION: Atlantic: north to Cape Cod, Massachusetts. Pacific: a species which is probably this runs south of our range.

COLOR: Greenish on back and upper sides, shading into gray-ish-gold on sides, and iridescent silvery, yellow, or gold under-neath. Dark spot on gill cover and faint dark blotch on base of pectoral fins.

DISTINGUISHING CHARACTERS: Breast naked except for a small patch of scales in front of the ventral fins. Spot on gill cover. No detached finlets. Lower jaw with pair of canine teeth on front. Long, curved pectoral fins.

SIZE: Two or 3 pounds; up to 20.

FOOD: Mullet and smaller fishes; crabs.

HABITS: Around bridges, pilings, etc., and in inlets. Also runs offshore. Small schools or groups.

Common Green Jack   *Caranx caballus* (Günther)

NAMES: Jurel.

DISTRIBUTION: North to San Pedro, California (rare); com-mon south of our range.

COLOR: Brownish-green on back and top of sides, head, tail, and ventral fins. Rest of body iridescent gilt-silver. Rest of fins light, with green tinge. Sometimes there are pale bars on the sides. Black spot on gill cover.

DISTINGUISHING CHARACTERS: The locality. Scaled breast. Spot on gill cover.

SIZE: Seldom over 15″.

FOOD: Fishes.

HABITS: Rare in our range.

Horse-eye Jack   *Caranx latus* Agassiz

NAMES: Crevalle, Goggle-eye Jack, Jurel, Jack.

DISTRIBUTION: North to Virginia; concentration is southward. Out of range in the Pacific.

COLOR: Blue on back and upper sides; gilt-silver below. Fins dusky.

DISTINGUISHING CHARACTERS: Breast covered with small scales. A small dark spot on the gill cover. Dorsal rays, 20 to 22; anal rays, 17 or 18. Large eye. The body is deeper than that of the Blue Runner.

SIZE: Usually under 2′ and 2 pounds, but has been reported up to 35 pounds.

FOOD: Smaller fishes, crabs, shrimps, crayfish.

HABITS: Around reefs near Gulf Stream in small schools.

Rainbow Runner *Elagatis bipinnulatus* (Quoy & Gaimard)

NAMES: Runner, Yellowtail, Skipjack, Shoemaker.

DISTRIBUTION: A Southern fish, nowhere common. Straggles north to New York. Out of range in the Pacific. *Plate 13.*

COLOR: Back and upper part of sides dark blue, margined below with a narrow light blue stripe running the length of the body; body then yellow to the mid-line of the sides, where this is margined below with another narrow light blue lengthwise line; rest of body silvery-yellow or yellowish; all fins yellowish.

DISTINGUISHING CHARACTERS: Color. A detached finlet behind dorsal and anal fins.

SIZE: Usually about 1′ long; reaches about 3′ and a weight of over 12 pounds.

FOOD: Fishes and crustaceans.

HABITS: Its habits are not well known.

THE POMPANOS: The Pacific pompanos are all south of our range. The three Atlantic species may be easily told apart as follows:

25 rays in the dorsal fin; 22 in the anal fin. . Common Pompano
19 to 20 rays in the dorsal; 17 to 19 in the anal. . . . . . . Permit
19 to 20 rays in the dorsal; 17 to 19 in the anal. Body round; dorsal fin lobe very long. . . . . Round Pompano

The adult pompanos have no teeth, and their dorsal spines are not connected to each other by membranes. In older specimens these spines may be sunk so low in the flesh as to be almost invisible. All of these fishes school or wander around in small groups.

Common Pompano   *Trachinotus carolinus* (Linnaeus)

Names: Permit, Carolina Pompano, Cobbler. *Plate 14.*

Distribution: Common from North Carolina south, and on the Gulf coast; occasionally straggles north to Cape Cod, Massachusetts, but rarely in an adult stage.

Color: Blue on upper sides; top of head darker blue; rest of body silvery with deep golden reflections. Dorsal fin dusky blue; pectorals and anal pale orange with touches of blue; caudal dusky blue with yellowish margin.

Distinguishing Characters: The rays of the dorsal and anal fins are more numerous than in the other pompanos.

Size: Reaches 1½′. The average weight is about 2 pounds or less.

Food: Mollusks, crustaceans, beach fleas, shrimps, minnows.

Habits: This is the well-known commercial Pompano. It is a Southern fish, common around banks, inlets, and river mouths and most abundant in winter.

Round Pompano   *Trachinotus falcatus* (Linnaeus)

Names: Indian River Permit, Palometa, Pompano, Small Permit. *Plate 14.*

Distribution: Straggles north in the Gulf Stream as far as Cape Cod, Massachusetts, when young, but common from North Carolina south and in the Gulf of Mexico.

Color: Bluish above; rest of body silvery; fins all blue with light tips.

Distinguishing Characters: Round body and long dorsal lobe.

Size: Reaches 1½′ and a weight of 3 pounds.

Food: Crustaceans, mollusks, minnows.

Habits: Banks, cuts, inlets.

Permit   *Trachinotus goodei* Jordan & Evermann

Names: Great Pompano, Big Pompano, Key West Permit, Pompano, Mexican Pompano, Palometa. *Plate 14.*

Distribution: North to Florida.

Color: Bluish over silver. All fins dark.

Distinguishing Characters: Nineteen to 20 rays in dorsal fin, 17 to 19 in anal. Body deep but not round; dorsal lobe not prolonged.

Size: The largest of the pompanos, reaching 6 to 8 pounds and a length of 3′.

Food: Mollusks, crustaceans, very small fishes.

Habits: Outer reefs and edge of Gulf Stream; shallow water around the Keys, and occasionally in surf.

COMMON POMPANO

ROUND POMPANO

PERMIT

PLATE 14

Amberjack   *Seriola lalandi* Valenciennes

NAMES: Great Amberjack, Coronado, Atlantic Amberjack, Amberfish.

DISTRIBUTION: North to Massachusetts, but commonly off Florida.

COLOR: Silvery, overlaid with light blue; bluer on back and upper sides. Fins dusky with pale yellow band near or on edges.

DISTINGUISHING CHARACTERS: Small scales. Very fine teeth on the tongue, roof of mouth, and in bands on the jaws.

SIZE: Averages about 10 to 15 pounds, but runs to over 100.

FOOD: Smaller fishes, such as grunts, mullet, etc.

HABITS: Offshore reefs, singly or in small, not closely schooling groups. Usually fished in winter and spring.

Pacific Yellowtail   *Seriola dorsalis* (Gill)

NAMES: Amberfish, Amberjack, Jack, California Yellowtail, Yellowtail, White Salmon. *Plate 15.*

DISTRIBUTION: Monterey, California, south; quite plentiful off San Diego.

COLOR: Light blue or greenish on back and upper sides; lower parts silvery. A conspicuous yellow band runs from the back of the eye to the tail. Fins yellowish.

DISTINGUISHING CHARACTERS: Scales and teeth as in Amberjack. The yellow horizontal band. Distribution. This is the only *Seriola* within our Pacific range.

SIZE: Averages up to 20 pounds; runs to over 80.

FOOD: Smaller schooling fishes and their young; crustaceans.

HABITS: Inshore on rocky shores, in schools or small groups. Off our California range it is most plentiful from March to June.

California Horse Mackerel
                        Trachurus symmetricus (Ayres)

NAMES: Spanish Mackerel, Saurel.

DISTRIBUTION: North to San Francisco, California; more plentiful around Los Angeles.

COLOR: Back and upper sides unevenly dark green; lower parts silver.

DISTINGUISHING CHARACTERS: The fish is mackerel-shaped, but there is a row of spiny plates running the entire length of the lateral line and becoming very conspicuous as they approach the tail. The lateral line decurves sharply about the middle of its length. There are no finlets as in the mackerels. The teeth are very small and in a single row on the jaws. Better known as a food

PACIFIC YELLOWTAIL

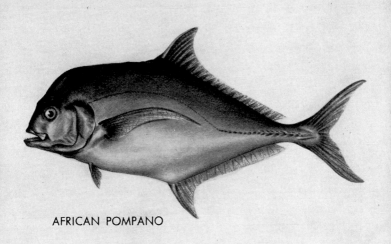

AFRICAN POMPANO

PLATE 15

fish than as a game fish, this should possibly not be included in our list. It may be the same as a species occurring off the Florida Keys—the Rough Scad.

African Pompano   *Hynnis cubensis* (Poey)

NAMES: Cuban Jack. *Plate 15.*

DISTRIBUTION: North to the Florida Keys.

COLOR: Silvery, with traces of light blue.

DISTINGUISHING CHARACTERS: Shape of body. Bony plates on posterior part of the lateral line.

SIZE: Reaches length of 3′ and has been recorded as weighing 35 pounds.

FOOD AND HABITS: The life history of this rare fish is not known. It is suspected of being the adult of another fish called the Threadfish, *Alectis ciliaris* (Bloch). The African Pompano has been taken a few times in our range off Florida, in winter.

Dolphin   *Coryphaena hippurus* Linnaeus

NAMES: Dorado, Dourade. *Color Plate 16.*

DISTRIBUTION: North to Cape Cod, Massachusetts; abundant from South Carolina to Texas. Pacific: north to northern Oregon.

COLOR: This fish shifts rapidly from one color phase to another but is always some combination of green, yellow, or blue, usually with dark spots.

DISTINGUISHING CHARACTERS: High straight forehead (particularly so in the males). Long dorsal fin without spines. Brilliant color.

SIZE: Reaches a weight of well over 60 pounds, but averages about 3 or 4.

FOOD: Smaller fishes, especially mullet and flying fishes. Makes spectacular leaps when in pursuit of food.

HABITS: Schools and solitary. A warm-water fish of the open ocean, frequent in blue water. Off our Pacific range in warm summers. Florida all year. On our Atlantic range stays in or near the Gulf Stream.

Bluefish   *Pomatomus saltatrix* (Linnaeus)

NAMES: Tailor, Snapping Mackerel, Snapper, Greenfish, Fatback. *Color Plate 17.*

DISTRIBUTION: North to Nova Scotia; abundant from Florida to Penobscot Bay, Maine, but not taken in the Bay of Fundy or off the Nova Scotian side of the Gulf of St. Lawrence.

DISTINGUISHING CHARACTERS: Distinct from its nearest rela-

DOLPHIN

PLATE 16

tives, the Crevalles, by having a row of large, strong, unequal teeth in each jaw.

SIZE: Averages about 2 pounds, but reaches 25.

FOOD: Very voracious; small fishes, squids.

HABITS: An erratic wanderer, moving in large schools but varying greatly in numbers in the same localities in different years, sometimes not appearing at all. Frequents water temperatures above 40°. The smaller individuals run up river mouths into brackish water.

Cobia   *Rachycentron canadus* (Linnaeus)

NAMES: Cabio, Sergeantfish, Crab-eater, Black Bonito, Coalfish, Lemonfish, Ling, Black Salmon. *Color Plate 17.*

DISTRIBUTION: Straggles north to Massachusetts, but not common north of Chesapeake Bay.

COLOR: The longitudinal dark stripe is much more distinct in some individuals; others run light in color—almost cream-colored.

DISTINGUISHING CHARACTERS: Longitudinal dark stripe. Separate, depressible pre-dorsal spines. Spindle-shaped body with flat head and large mouth.

SIZE: Averages about 10 pounds, but the rod-and-reel record is over 100.

FOOD: Crabs, squids, shrimps, smaller fishes, especially bottom fishes.

HABITS: Swims singly or with two or three others of its kind, sometimes among schools of other fishes. Open water and inlets, bays, etc.; often near pilings and mangroves. All year; common in summer on the Gulf coast.

Snook or Robalo   *Centropomus undecimalis* (Bloch)

NAMES: Brochet de Mer, Sergeantfish, Pike. *Color Plate 18.*

DISTRIBUTION: North to Florida; common in the Gulf of Mexico. Pacific robalos are all south of our limit.

DISTINGUISHING CHARACTERS: Black lateral line. Long body with projecting lower jaw.

SIZE: Averages about 4 pounds or less; runs to over 50.

FOOD: Mullet and other smaller fishes; crabs, shrimps.

HABITS: Sandy shores, inlets, mud flats. Often ascending rivers for some distance. All year.

Striped Bass   *Roccus saxatilis* (Walbaum)

NAMES: Rockfish, Greenhead, Striper, Streaked Bass, Rock, Squidhound. *Color Plate 18.*

DISTRIBUTION: Atlantic: Gulf of St. Lawrence to Florida and the Gulf; common from Cape Cod, Massachusetts, to North Carolina. Pacific: Monterey, California, to Coos Bay, Oregon; most common around San Francisco Bay and south.

COLOR: Often very brassy.

DISTINGUISHING CHARACTERS: Seven or 8 longitudinal stripes on the sides. Separate dorsal fins. Lower jaw projects slightly.

SIZE: Averages 1 to 10 pounds; 25 to 30 not rare; recorded at 125.

FOOD: Smaller fishes, crabs, shrimps.

HABITS: Goes into bays and rivers to spawn. Abundant in rivers in the winter and spring, but the larger ones are generally taken in the sea both around rocky shores, reefs, and bars, and in surf along beaches. Very seldom any distance offshore. Present all year, but sluggish in the colder weather. Runs in large schools.

California Black Sea Bass   *Stereolepis gigas* Ayres

NAMES: California Jewfish, Black Sea Bass, Giant Bass, Giant Sea Bass. *Color Plate 19.*

DISTRIBUTION: North to San Francisco Bay; more abundant about San Diego, California.

DISTINGUISHING CHARACTERS: More dorsal spines than dorsal rays; the spines all depressible in a groove; short, round pectorals.

SIZE: Said to reach 600 pounds; the angling record is 515. Rarely taken under 50.

FOOD: Fishes and crustaceans.

HABITS: Bottom-living, inshore around rocks. All year; the favorite angling season is summer.

Spotted Jewfish   *Promicrops itaiara* (Lichtenstein)

NAMES: Florida Jewfish, Southern Jewfish, Junefish, Giant Sea Bass, Giant Bass, Guasa, Mero, Black Grouper, Black Snapper, Jewfish, Black Jewfish, Grouper, Warsaw. *Color Plate 19.*

DISTRIBUTION: North to Florida. The Pacific distribution is south of our range.

COLOR: Very large specimens may lose most of the mottling.

DISTINGUISHING CHARACTERS: Color pattern. Very large head which is very broad between the eyes.

SIZE: Has been taken at 750 pounds, but averages considerably less and is often taken as low as 25.

FOOD: Fishes.

HABITS: Present most of the year off rocky shores and often around pilings, etc. A rather sluggish fish.

45

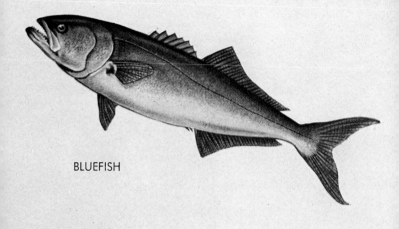

BLUEFISH

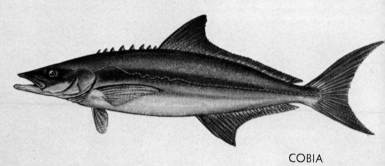

COBIA

PLATE 17

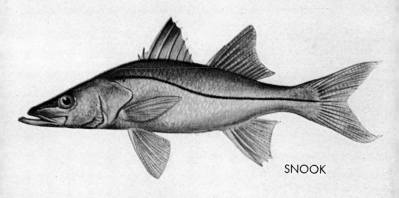

SNOOK

STRIPED BASS

PLATE 18

Sea Bass   *Centropristes striatus* (Linnaeus)

NAMES: Blackfish, Black Sea Bass, Hanahill, Black Will, Black Harry, Tally Wag, Humpback, Rock Bass.

DISTRIBUTION: Cape Ann, Massachusetts, south to northern Florida. Straggles to Maine. Abundant off New Jersey.

COLOR: Grayish-brown or gray; sometimes bluish-black; sometimes mottled. Horizontal narrow stripes. Dorsal fin with light bands and spots. Other fins dusky.

DISTINGUISHING CHARACTERS: A single, continuous dorsal fin composed of spiny and rayed portions of equal length. The tail fin is rounded, and there is a prolonged ray at its upper corner. Pectorals wide and rounded; anal with short spines. The anal base is short, but the rays are long and the margin of the fin is round. Ventrals begin in front of the beginning of the pectorals.

SIZE: Averages about 1½ pounds and rarely weighs more than 4.

FOOD: Smaller fishes, crabs, shrimps, lobsters, squids, barnacles. A bottom feeder.

HABITS: A Northern fish, both inshore and offshore. Apt to be found near or among rocks. Off New England is most abundant from July through September. Present most of the year in the South.

California Sand Bass   *Paralabrax nebulifer* Girard

NAMES: Rock Bass, California Rock Bass, Johnny Verde, Kelp Bass. *Color Plate 20.*

DISTRIBUTION: North to Monterey, California.

COLOR: The spots present on the head in young specimens disappear in the adult.

DISTINGUISHING CHARACTERS: No spots. The spiny and rayed parts of the dorsal fin are continuous. The third dorsal spine is noticeably higher than the others. The top of the head between the eyes is scaled as far forward as the front margin of the eyes.

SIZE: Reaches a length of about 18″.

HABITS: Over sandy bottom in shallow water.

NOTE: The species of *Paralabrax* are considerably confused by fishermen and often all called Rock Bass.

California Kelp Bass   *Paralabrax clathratus* (Girard)

NAMES: Rock Bass, Sand Bass, Cabrilla. *Color Plate 20.*

DISTRIBUTION: North to San Francisco, California.

DISTINGUISHING CHARACTERS: Third to fifth dorsal spines of about the same length. Very few scales on the head between the eyes. Snout pointed. No dots.

Size: Reaches 20″ and weight of 5 pounds; usually less.

Habits: Quite common, particularly fished in winter. Commonest in the kelp beds, where it feeds on small organisms found there.

Red-Spotted Rock Bass
Paralabrax maculatofasciatus (Steindachner)

Names: Spotted Cabrilla.

Distribution: North to Santa Barbara Channel, California.

Color: Greenish- or brownish-gray, much paler underneath; small red-brown spots on body except for belly, and on rayed dorsal and caudal fins. The ground color of the fins is usually a lighter shade than that of the body.

Distinguishing Characters: Spots. Very few scales on top of head. Third dorsal spine longer than the others.

Habits: Frequents bays and sandy shores.

THE GROUPERS are extremely hard to tell apart and are very often misidentified, due to similarity of structure and to their ability to change color instantaneously. Mr. L. S. Caine, author of *Game Fish of the South,* writes me that "there are probably only three groupers that are even considered by the sports fishermen down here: the Black Grouper, the Nassau Grouper, and the Red Grouper. Of these three, the Black Grouper is by all odds the most sporty of the lot."

For a set of color plates showing the various color phases the individual groupers are capable of assuming, see C. H. Townsend's "Records of Changes in Color among Fishes," *Zoologica* (*N. Y. Zool. Soc.*), 1929, Volume 9, Number 9, pp. 321–78; 27 color plates.

For difficult identification, the angler must depend on a reliable local person plus a technical reference.

The Pacific groupers all occur south of our limits.

Distinguishing Characters for the Groupers: Single, continuous dorsal fin of never less than 10 spines and rays; large mouth with canine teeth in front; projecting lower jaw. The genus *Mycteroperca* is broad on top of the head between the eyes; *Epinephalus* is narrow. The groupers do not move rapidly from place to place in schools, but hover in small groups over one spot.

Black Grouper   *Mycteroperca bonaci* (Poey)

Names: Warsaw, Jewfish, Black Rockfish, Gray Grouper, Grouper. *Color Plate 21.*

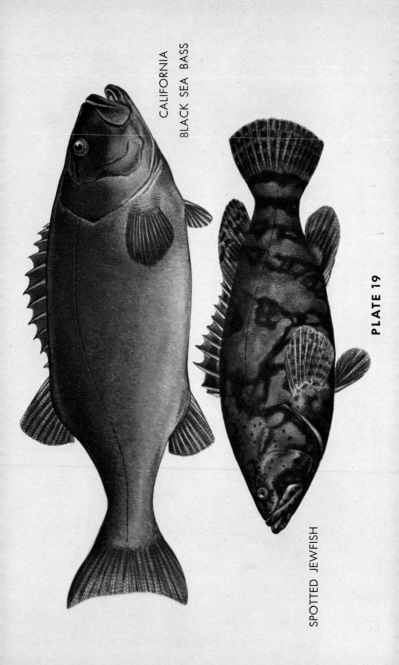

CALIFORNIA
BLACK SEA BASS

SPOTTED JEWFISH

PLATE 19

CALIFORNIA
SAND BASS

CALIFORNIA
KELP BASS

PLATE 20

DISTRIBUTION: North to Pensacola, Florida, and abundant at Key West; straggles north to Massachusetts.

COLOR: Can change color to dark reddish-gray with a few short black horizontal streaks on middle of sides or to pure white with a few dusky short bars and dots and dark-margined white fins or to very light gray with blue and brown horizontal bars and blue fin margins with traces of rosy on anal and throat!

DISTINGUISHING CHARACTERS: General characters of the group. About 110 scales in horizontal row from back of gill cover to base of tail. The dark phase is probably the most common and the most easily distinguishable.

SIZE: Maximum about 50 pounds; usually runs from 5 to 10.

FOOD: Mullet, grunts, and other fishes; crabs.

HABITS: Chiefly offshore banks and outer reefs.

Gag   *Mycteroperca microlepis* (Goode & Bean)

NAMES: Grouper.

DISTRIBUTION: North Carolina south, and Gulf coast.

COLOR: Changes as in other groupers. Most usual phase is brownish with a dusky green dorsal, usually with a white edge, and a black caudal with bright blue patches and a white edge. The anal in this phase is purple-blue with a white edge. Ventrals and pectorals are dusky. The fish is apt to be lighter in shallower water.

DISTINGUISHING CHARACTERS: Very small scales—about 140 in a longitudinal row.

SIZE: Averages about 3 pounds. Jordan and Evermann say it reaches about 50 pounds, and all subsequent authors appear to have adopted this figure.

FOOD: Mullet, grunts, and other small fishes; crabs.

HABITS: Chiefly offshore on banks and outside reefs.

Rock Grouper   *Mycteroperca venenosa apua* (Bloch)

NAMES: Bonaci Cardinal, Red Grouper, Rockfish, Grouper, Spotted Grouper.

This fish may be the same as the Yellow Grouper (see below), according to the late Dr. W. H. Longley, who did a great deal of work on the fishes of the Florida Keys. Its most frequent color phase is scarlet on the upper sides and grayish below, with small red spots on the upper parts and larger ones below. Dr. Longley says that numbers of this phase of the fish from deep water "became like those [the Yellow Grouper] from shallow water when they were confined with them." Other data on the "Rock Grouper" is the same as that on the Yellow Grouper.

Yellow Grouper   *Mycteroperca venenosa* (Linnaeus)

NAMES: Yellow-finned Grouper, Princess Rockfish, Rockfish, Red Grouper, Spotted Grouper, Gag, Bonaci di Piedra. *Color Plate 21.*

DISTRIBUTION: North to the Florida Keys.

COLOR: Other phases are pure white except for some vague grayish spots and indications of narrow dark dorsal and tail fin margins; white with distinct black dots all over the body; grayish-brown with dusky small bars in a longitudinal line on upper part of body and small red dots on lower sides and with a yellow margin on pectoral fin; white with similar but olive-green bars and small red dots all over the body, bright yellow dorsal spines and pectoral margin; the other fins dark-edged. The fish changes color rapidly and confusingly; it has been recorded by Dr. Longley as turning very dark over white sand when it was chasing a snapper and was momentarily stranded in shallows.

DISTINGUISHING CHARACTERS: Body rather heavy; scales very small—smaller than those of the Black Grouper (about 125 from gill cover to tail).

SIZE: Reaches a length of 1½′.

FOOD: As that of other groupers.

HABITS: Outside reefs and offshore banks.

Nassau Grouper   *Epinephelus striatus* (Bloch)

NAMES: Hamlet, Cherna Criolla, Gray Grouper, White Grouper, Rockfish, Grouper. *Color Plate 21.*

DISTRIBUTION: North to the Florida Keys.

COLOR: Different phases, ranging from solid white, through white with dark or light blue bands to the phase in the plate; or to orange-tan with dark bands; dark brown above and white below; solid, very dark gray-brown. On all the barred or blotched patterns, there is a stripe from in front of the eye running upward toward the dorsal fin. Townsend shows seven different color phases for this fish.

DISTINGUISHING CHARACTERS: Head narrow between the eyes. The eye-to-dorsal stripe.

SIZE: As in other groupers.

FOOD: As in other groupers.

HABITS: Most frequently found on the Florida Keys outside the belt of coral and sea fans.

Red Grouper *Epinephelus morio* (Cuvier & Valenciennes)

NAMES: Cherna americana, Mero, Grouper, Brown Snapper, Negre, Red-bellied Snapper, Red Snapper, Spotted Grouper, Cherna. *Color Plate 22.*

BLACK GROUPER

YELLOW GROUPER

NASSAU GROUPER

PLATE 21

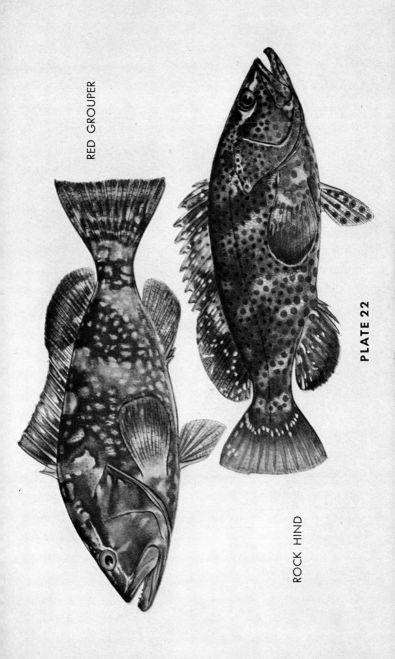

RED GROUPER

ROCK HIND

PLATE 22

DISTRIBUTION: North to Virginia.

COLOR: Many color phases, ranging from solid black to almost solid light red; pinkish tan; white with branching bands of pink; delicate, very light tannish-pink; pale gray.

DISTINGUISHING CHARACTERS: Its more northern range than any of the others.

SIZE: Said to reach 50 pounds or more.

FOOD: Other fishes, octopus, crabs, shrimps, and other small creatures. Always hungry; will feed from a diver's hand!

HABITS: The most common of the genus; very common in shallow water at Tortugas, also in deeper water on reefs where it can find cover.

Red Hind   *Epinephelus guttatus* (Linnaeus)

NAMES: Cabrilla, Coney, Hind, Polka Dot, Calico Hind, Grouper.

DISTRIBUTION: North to the Florida Keys and occasionally as far as Charleston, South Carolina (summer).

COLOR: Shifts color. May be white or light gray with red dots and white fins; or tannish-yellow with red dots, yellow spines in dorsal, yellowish-red pectoral, and other fins dark green, or whitish with red dots. There is also a color phase of four or five broad vertical green bands from the base of the dorsal fin about halfway down the sides.

DISTINGUISHING CHARACTERS: Small red dots all over the body; small size of the fish.

SIZE: Smaller than the others; rarely more than 1½′ long and usually less, with an average weight of 2 pounds, and, as far as we know, a maximum weight of not over 6.

FOOD: See other groupers.

HABITS: Most abundant south of our range; moderately deep water over reefs.

Rock Hind   *Epinephelus adscensionis* (Osbeck)

NAMES: Cabra Mora, Grouper, Hind, Speckled Hind, Polka Dot. *Color Plate 22.*

DISTRIBUTION: North to the Florida Keys.

COLOR: Various phases, but usually all have red dots and a good deal of green, particularly in the fins. Often there are large white spots or blotches. Roof of mouth often has red spots.

DISTINGUISHING CHARACTERS: Green fins; red dots; white spots.

SIZE: Averages about 2 pounds; runs from 6 to 8.

FOOD: See other groupers.

HABITS: Reefs and rocks.

Black Jewfish   *Garrupa nigrita* (Holbrook)

NAMES: Black Grouper, Mero de lo Alto. *Color Plate 23.*

DISTRIBUTION: North to Charleston, South Carolina.

COLOR: Ranges from that of the plate to chocolate brown; sometimes has faint pale blotches. Fins dark.

DISTINGUISHING CHARACTERS: Dark color; small eye; large size.

SIZE: Reported, probably truly, to reach a weight of 600 pounds and a length of 6'.

HABITS: Not uncommon off Florida and in the Gulf.

Coney   *Petrometopon cruentatus* (Lacépède)

NAMES: Red Hind, Graysby.

DISTRIBUTION: North to the Florida Keys; more common southward. South of our range in the Pacific.

COLOR: Red-gray with bright vermilion spots. Sometimes very dark, with small brown spots; sometimes lighter with bands. Rayed dorsal fin and tail fin narrowly edged with white.

DISTINGUISHING CHARACTERS: Lower jaw does not project very much. Tail fin rounded. Scales rather large, about 80, and very rough. The real characters are technical and lie in the peculiarities of some of the head bones.

SIZE: Reaches about 1'.

HABITS: Longley says this fish is not uncommon on caverned bottom east of East Key. Reef patches.

Sandfish   *Diplectrum formosum* (Linnaeus)

DISTRIBUTION: North to Charleston, South Carolina. Pacific specimens south of our limit.

COLOR: Changeable; apt to be grayish with longitudinal brown stripes, a very conspicuous one from snout to base of tail and ending in a black spot; another from the eye to the end of the dorsal base.

DISTINGUISHING CHARACTERS: Dorsal fin has no notch between the spines and the rays.

SIZE: Reaches about 1'.

HABITS: Channels—of approximately 10 fathoms—within lagoons; smooth sandy or mud bottoms.

Tripletail   *Lobotes surinamensis* (Bloch)

NAMES: Flasher, Lumpfish, Sea Perch, Chobie, Buoyfish, Black Tripletail. *Color Plate 23.*

DISTRIBUTION: North to Cape Cod, Massachusetts. Pacific species south of limit. Found most often on Florida and Texas coasts.

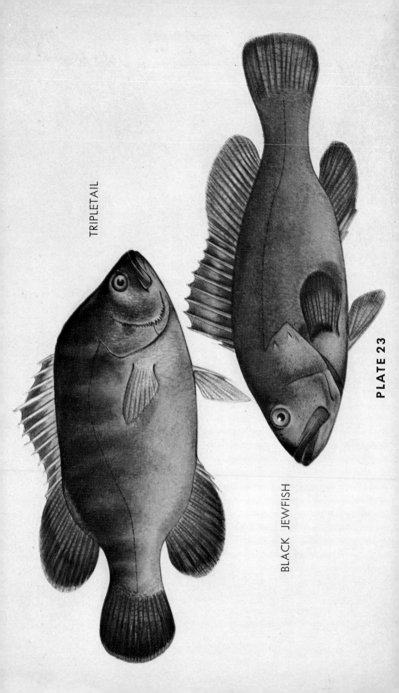

TRIPLETAIL

BLACK JEWFISH

PLATE 23

COLOR: Shade varies from lighter to darker.

DISTINGUISHING CHARACTERS: No teeth on roof of mouth. Rounded dorsal, anal, and tail fins. Upper jaws very protractile. Bases of rayed dorsal and anal fins thickened and scaly.

SIZE: Reaches 3', but averages shorter and about 7 pounds.

FOOD: Mullet and other small fishes; crabs, clams, mussels.

HABITS: Solitary. Usually open water, fairly deep. Seeks cover around buoys, etc. Varies in abundance from year to year. Present from South Carolina to Florida all year, but farther north only in summer.

THE SNAPPERS school; the Groupers do not. The Pacific Snappers are all south of our range.

Schoolmaster   *Lutianus apodus* (Walbaum)

NAMES: Caji, Sea Lawyer, Black Snapper, Gray Snapper, Dog Snapper. *Plate 24.*

DISTRIBUTION: North to Florida; young sometimes straggle farther north in the Gulf Stream.

COLORS: Brownish-red above; red-orange below. Often has light bars from ridge of back down the sides. Fins yellow. Sometimes has a blue streak diagonally from snout through eye to upper part of gill cover.

DISTINGUISHING CHARACTERS: Rather deep body. Distance between end of snout and front of eye very long, and that line of profile steep and straight until past the eye. The scales large. A very large canine tooth on either side of the upper jaw.

SIZE: Averages 2 pounds; reaches 8.

FOOD: Crabs, shrimps, small fishes.

HABITS: Very abundant. Often on grounds with Gray Snapper during the day but feeding separately at night. Inshore and offshore reefs; around wharves.

Lane Snapper   *Lutianus synagris* (Linnaeus)

NAMES: Red-tail Snapper, Biajaiba, Spot Snapper. *Plate 24.*

DISTRIBUTION: North to Florida.

COLOR: Rosy above, shading to olive-silvery below. A conspicuous dark red blotch on side. May be gray above and silvery below, but the blotch remains. May also show traces of bands or yellow longitudinal stripes. Dorsal and tail red; other fins yellow.

DISTINGUISHING CHARACTERS: Blotch on side. Lower jaw projects. Tail not deeply forked. Sixty scales in a row from gill cover to tail base.

SIZE: Usually less than 1'. Reaches 4 pounds.

Food: Smaller fishes; crabs.

Habits: Occasionally solitary. Creek mouths, inlets, and around wharves. In the Gulf of Mexico caught in company with the Red Snapper.

Muttonfish   *Lutianus analis* (Cuvier & Valenciennes)

Names: Pargo, Sama, Red Snapper, Green Snapper, Pargo Criolla. *Plate* 24.

Distribution: North to Florida, straying north to Massachusetts in Gulf Stream. Occasionally taken off Texas.

Color: Banded when on bottom, changing to tan with wormlike markings when swimming. Sometimes dark with conspicuous bars, which may suddenly fade out. Most usual color phase is dark olive on back, shading into light red and then pinkish-white. Scales in younger specimens have light blue dots forming streaks running up and back. Sometimes narrow, dark, vertical bars and a dark spot on side. Fins red except dorsal, which is yellow with reddish tips.

Distinguishing Characters: Dark spot. Brick-red fins. Small scales.

Size: Averages about 4 pounds but runs to 25.

Food: Fishes, crustaceans.

Habits: Usually on outer reefs. All year, but least frequent in July and August.

Dog Snapper   *Lutianus jocu* (Bloch & Schneider)

Names: Jocu, Pargo Colorado.

Distribution: North to Florida and straggling farther north in the Gulf Stream.

Color: Ground color coppery red, overlaid with olive; usually a blue stripe below eye. Faint indications of dark and light crossbars on body. Fins light red except tail, which is yellowish.

Distinguishing Characters: Less orange than the Schoolmaster; more olive than the Gray Snapper; no dark spot. Snout longer than that of the Muttonfish. Longley says, "The most distinctive mark, when displayed, is the light-colored triangular blaze on the cheek."

Size: Averages under 2 pounds, but reported to run up to 110!

Habits: Fairly deep water near reefs, wreckage, etc. Taken off the reefs off Texas in summer; fall and winter off Key West.

Pensacola Red Snapper
Lutianus blackfordii (Goode & Bean)

This fish is not a game fish. It is caught on hand lines. It is here

SCHOOLMASTER

LANE SNAPPER

MUTTONFISH

PLATE 24

inserted for identification purposes. It is deep brick red all over, including the fins. Center of abundance is the Gulf of Mexico. Found as far north as Long Island, N.Y. A famous food fish.

Mangrove Snapper *Lutianus griseus* (Linnaeus)

NAMES: Gray Snapper, Pargo Prieto, Pensacola Snapper, Red Snapper, Bastard Snapper, Lawyer. *Plate 25.*

DISTRIBUTION: North to New Jersey; common off Florida and Texas.

COLOR: Changeable. Gray; mahogany brown; brassy and green with red or gray sides. Dorsal fin dusky, caudal blackish purple or red, anal with a white edge, pectorals pale pink, ventrals white with red streaks. Redder in deep water.

DISTINGUISHING CHARACTERS: Rather long body. Blackish dorsal and anal rays. Tail slightly concave on the margin.

SIZE: Three to 5 pounds, running to 18.

FOOD: Crabs, small fishes. Off wharves it eats anything thrown into the water, including bread, beans, and potatoes.

HABITS: Shallow water in summer; deeper in winter. Wharves; coral heads offshore; submerged ledges; inland bays and sometimes surf. Except around wharves it feeds at night, but will bite during the day.

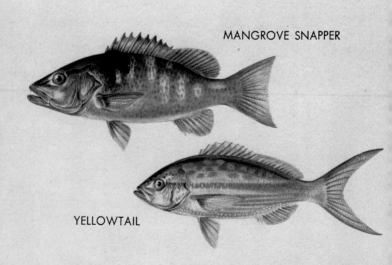

MANGROVE SNAPPER

YELLOWTAIL

PLATE 25

Yellowtail　　　　　　　　*Ocyurus chrysurus* (Bloch)

NAMES: Rabirubia, Snapper. *Plate 25.*

DISTRIBUTION: North to Florida.

COLOR: Variable, the yellow parts varying to pale straw; pattern sometimes blotched. Most usual color: grayish-blue with yellow spots and lines. A broad yellow stripe from snout to tail fin where it spreads. Lower parts of body rosy. Fins yellow.

DISTINGUISHING CHARACTERS: Color. Yellow fins. Deeply forked tail with long pointed lobes. Top of head has no scales.

SIZE: Averages under 1′ but reaches 2 or more.

FOOD: Feeds both day and night at surface and below and in lagoons, on smaller fishes, shrimps, crabs, etc.

HABITS: Very abundant in channels among the Keys. A fish of medium depths in inlets, lagoons, and shoals. Goes to deeper water in winter.

THE GRUNTS: Group characters: bright red mouth lining in some; continuous dorsal fin of spines and rays; scales on dorsal and anal rays. Scales near lateral line not parallel to it. No teeth on roof of mouth. Bands of conical teeth in jaws. These fishes move both in large schools, particularly at spawning time, and in small groups. All the Pacific grunts are out of our range.

Bastard Margaret Grunt　　*Haemulon parra* (Desmarest)

NAMES: Sailor's Choice, Ronco Blanco, Ronco Prieto, Brown Grunt, Ronco, Bastard Margaret.

DISTRIBUTION: North to Florida; abundant at Key West.

COLOR: Gray with iridescence or shading. Scales have small brown spots which form wavy streaks obliquely below the lateral line. Usually no spots on head. Black spot on gill cover. Fins dark gray. Mouth lining bright red.

DISTINGUISHING CHARACTERS: Oblique streaks. Back arched and profile rising steeply from snout to front of eye. Rays of dorsal, anal, and pectoral fins covered with scales.

SIZE: Maximum about 1′ and 21 pounds; average is less.

FOOD: Feeds at night on algae, mollusks, smaller fishes.

HABITS: Schools, small groups, or alone. Near reef bottoms for spawning in summer. Channels, inlets, mangrove roots.

French Grunt　　*Haemulon flavolineatum* (Desmarest)

NAMES: Open-mouthed Grunt, Ronco Contenado.

DISTRIBUTION: North to the Florida Keys, but more common southward.

COLOR: Ground color gray-blue. Longitudinal yellow or brassy stripes above the lateral line and obliquely below it. A stripe crosses the others, running from the head to end of the dorsal base. Fins bright yellow. Corner of mouth black, its lining bright red. Black spot on the gill cover.

DISTINGUISHING CHARACTERS: The color. Scales much larger toward front of body below the lateral line. Small mouth.

SIZE: Greatest length seems to be about 1'; usually is nearer 8".

FOOD: Feeds chiefly at night on invertebrates.

HABITS: Ledges, coral patches, and also near sandy shores.

Gray Grunt   *Haemulon macrostomum* Günther

NAMES: Striped Grunt, Flannelmouth, Black Grunt, Spanish Grunt, Pigfish, Redmouth, Squirrelfish.

DISTRIBUTION: North to Florida; not abundant.

COLOR: Dull silver with more or less distinct dark stripes above, the top one bounds the ridge of the back. Between this and the next is a yellowish area. Black spot on gill cover. Ventrals dusky; other fins rather intense yellow. Inside of mouth pale pink.

DISTINGUISHING CHARACTERS: Dark stripes. Second spine of anal fin very long. Large mouth.

SIZE: Averages about 1 pound, but has been reported to reach a length of 14", which must have weighed considerably more.

FOOD: Feeds at night on small fishes, crabs, starfish, sea urchins.

HABITS: Not abundant. Reefs and rocky shoals in water from 6' to 18'. Often in groups of other grunts.

Margate Fish   *Haemulon album* Cuvier & Valenciennes

NAMES: Margaret Grunt, Margate, Margate Grunt, Margotfish, Pompon, Sailor's Choice, Bream, Marketfish. *Plate 26.*

DISTRIBUTION: North to the Florida Keys.

COLOR: Subject to rapid change. Most usual phase very light pearl gray. Dark spots on the scales form widely spaced dotted longitudinal lines most distinct on upper sides. May also have a dusky lateral band. The fish may turn greenish if disturbed. Mouth vermilion inside; lips yellowish. Fins light olive green.

DISTINGUISHING CHARACTERS: Color and shape. Back more elevated and compressed than in other grunts. Profile steep to front of eye, then steeply curved to beginning of dorsal. Scales above lateral line in a very oblique arrangement.

SIZE: Averages 1 to 2 pounds; runs up to 10 pounds and a length of over 2'.

FOOD: Small fishes, crabs, sand fleas, etc.

HABITS: Rocky bottoms and coral, offshore; also sandy bottoms and around wrecks. Deep water except when feeding.

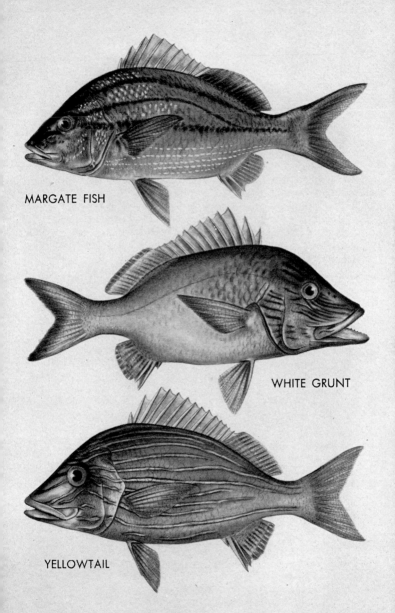

MARGATE FISH

WHITE GRUNT

YELLOWTAIL

PLATE 26

Yellow Grunt   *Haemulon sciurus* (Shaw)

NAMES: Blue-striped Grunt, Boar Grunt, Humpback Grunt, Ronco Amarillo. *Plate 26.*

DISTRIBUTION: North to the Florida Keys, where it is quite common at Key West.

COLOR: Variable. Mouth blood-red inside. Most frequent color phase is alternating stripes of blue and yellow, with pale blue lines on head from snout to eye. Spinous dorsal fin black edged with yellow. Rays of dorsal and most of tail fin black. Edge of tail fin yellow. Other fins yellow. The iris is gilt. Another phase is gray, or mottled gray, with much lighter fins.

DISTINGUISHING CHARACTERS: Color pattern of yellow and blue. Strong teeth.

SIZE: Average up to 3 pounds. Said to reach a length of 16″.

FOOD: Feeds at night, on crustaceans, mollusks, and worms.

HABITS: Common around the Keys. Schools or small groups about corals, sea fans, or over rocky bottoms. The schools break up at night and scatter to feed. Adults very abundant in August.

White Grunt   *Haemulon plumieri* (Lacépède)

NAMES: Boca Colorado, Black Grunt, Boar Grunt, Common Grunt, Ronco, Ronco Grande, Squirrelfish, Cachicata. *Plate 26.*

DISTRIBUTION: North to Cape Hatteras, North Carolina; most common near Key West, Florida, and on the Gulf coast.

COLOR: Changeable. Most commonly alternating stripes of blue and brassy. Over sand the fish is apt to be straw color and over corals dusky. Blue wavy stripes on head.

DISTINGUISHING CHARACTERS: The stripes, when present, on the head. Scales larger on upper front of body above the lateral line than on rest of body.

SIZE: Averages 1 pound; runs to 4.

FOOD: Feeds at night on crustaceans, worms, etc.

HABITS: Abundant on sandy shores. Caught all year off Key West. Appears in huge schools when spawning.

Pigfish   *Orthopristis chrysopterus* (Linnaeus)

NAMES: Piggie, Sailor's Choice, Hogfish. *Plate 27.*

DISTRIBUTION: Long Island (or north); common in Florida, Chesapeake Bay, Virginia, and Texas.

COLOR: Light blue and silver. Brown spots on snout. Blue streak on side of upper lip. Blue scale centers and bronze spots on their edges form oblique stripes above and horizontal stripes below lateral line. Brown spot on gill cover. Mouth whitish inside.

Dorsal fin spotted with bronze. Pectorals, ventrals, and base of tail yellow, dusky tipped. Anal light.

DISTINGUISHING CHARACTERS: Oblique stripes. Small scales, which are not parallel to lateral line above. Dorsal of fairly even height; spines slender. Jaw teeth in bands.

SIZE: Reaches 15″.

FOOD: Crustaceans, mollusks, beach fleas, marine worms, young fishes. A bottom feeder.

HABITS: Sandy shoals over grass, or rocky bars.

Pompon   *Anisotremus surinamensis* (Bloch)

NAMES: Black Margate, Margate Fish, Margate Grunt, Marketfish, Nassau Grunt, Sailor's Choice, Sea Bream. *Plate 27.*

DISTRIBUTION: North to Florida.

COLOR: Usually gray, with dark fins and a broad dark band encircling the body just under the pectoral fin. Fins all dusky. Rays of dorsal and anal very dark. The band is sometimes lacking.

DISTINGUISHING CHARACTERS: Continuous dorsal. Large scales.

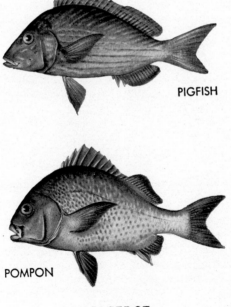

PIGFISH

POMPON

PLATE 27

No teeth on roof of mouth or on tongue. Mouth small; lips thick. Mouth not red inside. Tail fin usually more crescent-shaped than forked. Profile from snout to dorsal fin high. Dark girdle.

SIZE: Averages 1 to 2 pounds; reaches 3.
FOOD: Crabs, sand fleas, other crustaceans, and minnows.
HABITS: Inside rocky shoals; deep holes; channels.

Porkfish   *Anisotremus virginicus* (Linnaeus)

NAMES: Sisi, Porkie, Catalineta.
DISTRIBUTION: North to Florida; common at Key West.
COLOR: Bluish or dull silver, with conspicuous broad, bright yellow, longitudinal stripes. A black bar from beginning of the dorsal fin to behind the pectoral, and another from the top of the head, through the eye, to the corner of the mouth. The parts of the iris left exposed by this bar are yellow. Fins yellow. A scaly sheath at base of the anal is intensely yellow.
DISTINGUISHING CHARACTERS: The two black bars.
SIZE: Averages under 1 pound; runs to 2.
FOOD: Mollusks, crustaceans, small fishes.
HABITS: Schools for spawning in July and August in the shoals, after which it goes to deeper water.

Sargo   *Anisotremus davidsoni* (Steindachner)

DISTRIBUTION: North to San Diego, California.
COLOR: Silvery, usually with dark spots, particularly on head. A black band from mid-base of dorsal fin to the dark base of the pectoral. Edge of gill cover black. Fins yellowish.
DISTINGUISHING CHARACTERS: Black markings.
SIZE: Reaches 1′ in length.
HABITS: Not taken abundantly; usually in summer and fall.

Northern Porgy   *Stenotomus chrysops* (Linnaeus)

NAMES: Scup, Common Scup, Scuppaug, Paugy. *Plate 28*.
DISTRIBUTION: A Northern fish, from South Carolina to Cape Cod, Massachusetts, and straggling to Eastport, Maine.
COLOR: Brownish on the back and upper sides; silvery below this, with very bright patches. Fins unevenly dusky.
DISTINGUISHING CHARACTERS: Spiny part of dorsal higher and longer than the rays. Eye high in head. Top of head, snout, and chin without scales. Scaly sheath at bases of dorsal and anal rays. Front teeth narrow incisors. Tail margin deeply concave.
SIZE: Averages 1′ or less, and about 1½ pounds. Said to reach 1½′ and 3 or 4 pounds.
FOOD: A bottom feeder. Crabs, squids, clams, fish fry.
HABITS: Irregular in appearance but apt to appear in enormous

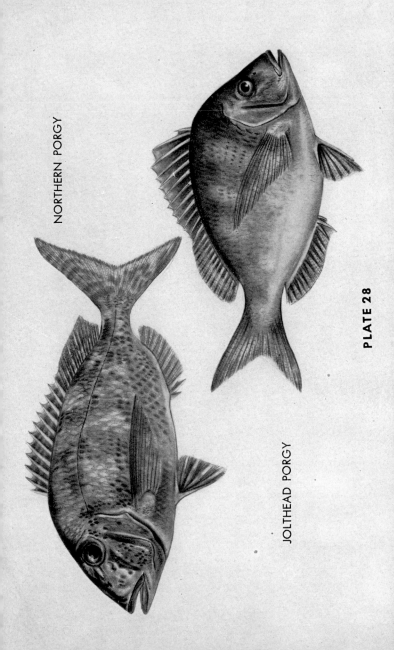

NORTHERN PORGY

JOLTHEAD PORGY

PLATE 28

schools in June to September. Prefers sandy bottoms in coastwise waters, swimming in 2 to 15 fathoms, but also at surface.

Southern Porgy or Fair Maid
Stenotomus aculeatus (Cuvier & Valenciennes)

DISTRIBUTION: From Cape Hatteras, North Carolina, southward, including Texas. This form closely resembles the Northern Porgy, which it replaces in this Southern range.

The four porgies following are tropical, inshore, schooling fishes, running north to the Florida Keys. The Grass Porgy is also taken off Pensacola, Florida. All have more or less the same body form (see plates) and all have conical teeth on front of the jaws. They are daytime feeders on crabs, squid, mollusks, and smaller fishes. They may be found around reefs, rocks, and also over sandy bottoms. Their chief non-technical difference lies in the color patterns.

The Saucer-Eye Porgy, Littlehead Porgy, and Jolthead Porgy have rather small scales (54 to 58 in the lateral line); the Grass Porgy's scales number 45 to 53. The Saucer-Eye and Littlehead are comparatively deep-bodied; the Jolthead more elongate.

These fishes are small, usually less than a pound, except the Jolthead, which is known to run to 10 pounds maximum.

Jolthead Porgy   *Calamus bajonado* (Bloch & Schneider)

NAMES: Bajonado. *Plate 28.*
COLOR: Brassy, with small gleaming scale spots. A narrow blue stripe below the eye and sometimes other blue marks on the head. Corner of the mouth purple and yellow. Fins dusky.
Very abundant.

Saucer-Eye Porgy
Calamus calamus (Cuvier & Valenciennes)

COLOR: Silvery and blue, with golden scale spots forming horizontal stripes. Brassy spots on head. A pearly stripe on the gill cover. Streak below eye, head in front of eye, and lower jaw dark violet. Fins pale, with vague orange blotches. Iris golden. Not as plentiful as the Jolthead or Littlehead.

Littlehead Porgy   *Calamus proridens* Jordan & Gilbert

COLOR: This fish looks very much like the Saucer-Eye but is silvery, with very bright gleaming patches. Blue-violet scale spots form horizontal stripes above the middle of the sides; the lower sides are spotted with pale orange. *Plate 29.*

LITTLEHEAD PORGY

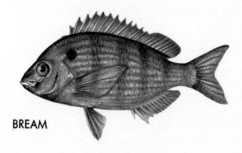

BREAM

PLATE 29

Grass Porgy   *Calamus arctifrons* Goode & Bean

NAMES: Shad Porgy.

COLOR: Olive, with dark bars and spots. Some pearly scale spots. Six yellow spots along the lateral line. Golden-yellow marks in front of the eye. Fins barred and spotted. This color varies somewhat, and dark bars running from the ridge of back to the belly are sometimes more, sometimes less distinct. A very small fish.

Bream   *Lagodon rhomboides* (Linnaeus)

NAMES: Salt-water Bream, Pinfish, Chopa Spina, Hogfish, Pig-fish, Porgy, Robin, Sargo, Scup, Sea Bream, Shiner, Shiny Scup, Spot, Squirrelfish, Yellowtail, Sailor's Choice. (Names are from L. S. Caine.) *Plate 29.*

DISTRIBUTION: North to Cape Cod, Massachusetts; very common southward and on the Gulf coast of Florida.

COLOR: Back olive green. Ground color bluish-silvery. A clear, black spot at shoulder behind gill cover. Sometimes about six vertical bands. Gilt horizontal stripes which tend to meet near

71

tail. Dorsal bluish, with a horizontal gilt band and a gilt margin; anal fin blue with a yellow stripe; tail fin yellow with traces of bars. Ventrals yellow; pectorals either colorless or dusky, transparent.

DISTINGUISHING CHARACTERS: The chief difference between this and the Sheepshead is a technical skull character. Color. Teeth in the front of the mouth are deeply notched incisors. No teeth on roof of mouth.

SIZE: Averages about 6″ and not known to exceed 10″.

FOOD: Smaller fishes, clams, crabs, barnacles, mollusks.

HABITS: Bays and inlets, particularly on the Florida coasts; feeds around pilings, mangroves, etc., in rather shallow water.

Sheepshead   *Archosargus probatocephalus* (Walbaum)

DISTRIBUTION: Cape Cod, Massachusetts (occasionally straggling to the Bay of Fundy), south; Florida and Gulf (all year); Texas (summer). May to November farther north. *Plate 30.*

COLOR: Olive on back and upper sides; rather dull silvery below. Seven wide black bands around the body, these becoming less distinct in the larger specimens. No distinct shoulder spot.

DISTINGUISHING CHARACTERS: Black bands when visible. Strong unnotched incisor teeth. None on roof of mouth. Resembles Northern Porgy, but tail margin less concave. The dorsal spines are alternately strong and slender.

SIZE: Larger northward; averages 3 to 6 pounds. Reaches 20.

FOOD: Barnacles, mussels. A bottom feeder.

HABITS: Pilings, wharves, and wrecks, etc., in search of food. Often goes up rivers into fresh water.

Rudderfish   *Kyphosus sectatrix* (Linnaeus)

NAMES: Bermuda Chub, Chopa, Chopa Blanca.

DISTRIBUTION: North to Cape Cod, Massachusetts; fairly common southward, especially off Key West, Florida.

COLOR: Steel gray, with bluish-gray and yellowish horizontal stripes. Fins dark gray. There may be vague small spots. Markings frequently indistinct.

DISTINGUISHING CHARACTERS: The spiny and rayed portions of its single dorsal fin are almost even in height throughout. There are flat, unnotched incisor teeth in the front of the jaws of the small mouth. The fish is quite deep-bodied.

SIZE: Averages 3 or 4 pounds; reaches 18″ and 9 pounds.

FOOD AND HABITS: Eats algae chiefly. The fish gets its name from its habit of following vessels for long distances, presumably feeding on their waste.

Swims in large schools and prefers shoals in channels.

SHEEPSHEAD

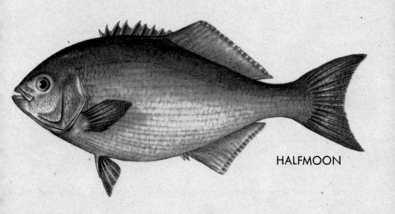

HALFMOON

PLATE 30

Halfmoon   *Medialuna californiensis* (Steindachner)

DISTRIBUTION: Point Conception, California, south. *Plate 30.*

COLOR: Very dark slate gray with a metallic sheen, becoming lighter and sometimes mottled below. Fins dusky. Sometimes there are faint, oblique, dotted lines on the sides.

DISTINGUISHING CHARACTERS: Rayed portions of dorsal and anal fins very heavily scaled. Rayed part of dorsal longer than the spiny part. Very small teeth on roof of mouth. The teeth in the first row of the jaw are not notched. The scales are uneven in size.

SIZE: Up to 1'.

FOOD: Herbivorous, chiefly algae.

HABITS: Present all year on rocky coasts.

Opal-Eye   *Girella nigricans* (Ayres)

This rudderfish is also found on rocky shores from San Francisco, California, southward. It lacks the heavily scaled dorsal and anal rays of the Halfmoon. It may be either light or dark olive green, and is further distinguished by its opalescent blue eyes. There are no teeth on the roof of its mouth; the outer row of teeth in the jaw are three-pointed.

CROAKERS derive their name from the peculiar sound made by some of them.

Never more than two spines in the anal fin. No incisor teeth, roof of the mouth, or tongue teeth. Powerful teeth in the throat. Lateral line onto tail. None of them frequent deep water or rocks.

Queenfish   *Seriphus politus* Ayres

NAMES: White Croaker, Herring.

DISTRIBUTION: North to Point Conception, California, and sometimes to San Francisco.

COLOR: Bluish-silvery on back and upper sides; rest of body silvery, sometimes with very fine dark dots. Fins bright yellow. Base of pectoral fin black.

DISTINGUISHING CHARACTERS: Second dorsal shorter than the anal. Rays of the dorsal and anal closely scaled. Fins fragile. A narrow band of teeth in the upper jaw; a single row in the lower. Center of lower jaw has a knob which fits into a notch in the upper jaw. Margin of the tail fin is concave.

SIZE: Reaches 1'.

FOOD: Smaller fishes.

HABITS: A schooling fish. Shallow water near sandy shores.

Weakfish   *Cynoscion regalis* (Bloch & Schneider)

NAMES: Squeteague, Sea Trout, Summer Trout, Gray Trout, Sun Trout, Shad Trout, Trout (particularly in the South), Squit, Drummer, Gray Squeteague. *Color Plate 31.*

DISTRIBUTION: Massachusetts Bay (straggling north) south to the east coast of Florida. According to Dr. Ginsburg, who has made a study of these fishes, this fish probably does not occur on the Gulf coast. (*See* Sand Squeteague.)

COLOR: Lower fins may be orange-yellow or gray.

DISTINGUISHING CHARACTERS: Very easily torn flesh and mouth. Dorsal fins are separate, the first higher and shorter than the second. There are 26 to 29 dorsal rays. The anal fin is short. The rayed dorsal and anal are scaled, but these scales easily rub off. The margin of the tail fin is only slightly concave. There are 2 large canine teeth in the upper jaw. The lower jaw projects beyond the upper.

SIZE: Averages 2 to 5 pounds; 8 and 9 not unusual off New Jersey in the fall. Reported to achieve 20.

FOOD: Squids, shrimps; chiefly herring, scup, menhaden, butter-fish, mummichogs, etc.

HABITS: Schools. Fond of tide rips, surf, channels, and inlets. Present all year from the Carolinas south; seasonal north of that, running coastwise inshore spring to late fall (May to October), when there are big runs off Long Island and New Jersey.

Spotted Weakfish
Cynoscion nebulosus (Cuvier & Valenciennes)

NAMES: Spotted Squeteague, Spotted Sea Trout, Speckled Sea Trout (also any of the names used for the Weakfish).

DISTRIBUTION: New York to Texas; rare north of Virginia; common southward.

COLOR: Much like that of the Weakfish. Conspicuous black spots on rays of the dorsal, on the tail fin, and on body, particularly on the upper part of sides below the beginning of the dorsal and running toward the tail. Dark above, silvery below; anal fin dusky as contrasted with the yellowish anal fin of the Weakfish.

DISTINGUISHING CHARACTERS: Color. No scales on rayed dorsal and anal fins. Two large canine teeth on tip of the upper jaw.

SIZE: Averages as in the Weakfish. Has been reported over 16 pounds.

FOOD: Like that of Weakfish.

HABITS: Resident, fairly common, running into brackish water. Sand shallows and mud flats.

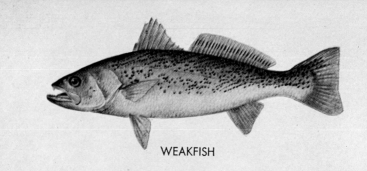

WEAKFISH

CALIFORNIA WHITE SEA BASS

SILVER PERCH

PLATE 31

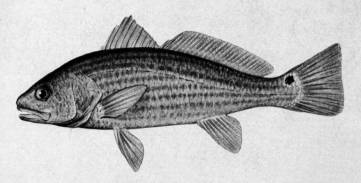

CHANNEL BASS

YELLOWFIN CROAKER

PLATE 32

Sand Squeteague   *Cynoscion arenarius* Ginsburg

NAMES: Sand Trout, White Trout (and probably also Weakfish).

DISTRIBUTION: Gulf coast; Atlantic coast (?).

COLOR: Dusky yellow above; pale silvery below. Spots, if present, are very indistinct. Tips of snout and lower jaw blackish.

DISTINGUISHING CHARACTERS: Margin of the tail double concave (middle rays longest). Long snout and never less than 10 rays in the anal fin.

HABITS: In the Gulf, occurs in the same waters with the Silver Squeteague but appears to run in shallower water.

This fish, according to Dr. Ginsburg, is the larger and more common of two species found on the Gulf coast. It is very much like the Weakfish (*Cynoscion regalis*) and might be a subspecies of it.

The other species is the:

Silver Squeteague   *Cynoscion nothus* (Holbrook)

NAMES: Sand Trout, Bastard Trout.

DISTRIBUTION: Chesapeake Bay to Florida, straggling on to the Gulf coast.

COLOR: Pale; tan above, silvery below; sometimes has irregular rows of dots on the upper sides.

DISTINGUISHING CHARACTERS: Usually 8 or 9 rays in the anal fin; very seldom 10, and if so, only in the Atlantic coast specimens.

California White Sea Bass   *Cynoscion nobilis* (Ayres)

NAMES: White Sea Bass, Santa Catalina Salmon.

DISTRIBUTION: North to Puget Sound, Washington, but not common north of San Francisco, California. Most abundant from Santa Barbara, California, southward. *Color Plate 31.*

COLOR: Walford describes this fish as "entirely metallic; bluish-gray above, frosted silvery below."

DISTINGUISHING CHARACTERS: No scales on the rays of dorsal or anal. Canine teeth small or usually missing in adult. Pectoral fin more than half the length of the head from tip of snout to back of gill cover.

SIZE: Reaches 80 pounds. Said to grow much larger.

FOOD: Herring, flying fishes, and other smaller fishes; crabs, squids, shrimps.

HABITS: All year. Most abundant April to September. Around islands, close inshore, and in kelp beds.

Shortfin Sea Bass   *Cynoscion parvipinnis* Ayres

This might be confused with the California White Sea Bass but may be distinguished by small dark dots all over the back and sides; white lower fins; a pair of canine teeth at the front of the upper jaw. It is a smallish, schooling fish, running north as far as Santa Barbara, California, but not common within our limits.

Silver Perch   *Bairdiella chrysura* (Lacépède)

This fish generally runs small but may reach 1' in length. It is not usually listed as a game fish but appears so in a Texas list (Reed, C. T., *Marine Life in Texas Waters*, 1941, p. 76) and is here included for that reason and because it is often confused with the White Perch.

NAMES: Yellowtail, Mademoiselle. *Color Plate 31*.

DISTRIBUTION: New York to Texas.

DISTINGUISHING CHARACTERS: Two anal spines and a lateral line that runs nearly to the end of the tail fin. Outer row of canine teeth in the upper jaw. The dorsal and anal rays are partially scaled. The curved-edged bone in front of the gill cover is edged with spines, the bottom one pointing abruptly downward.

HABITS: Abundant on sandy shores; present inshore in the North in summer; assumed to move offshore in the colder months.

Channel Bass   *Sciaenops ocellatus* (Linnaeus)

NAMES: Red Drum, Redfish, Bull Redfish, Redfin, Pez Colorado, Pescado Colorado, Reef Bass, Red Horse, Red Bass, Bar Bass, Beardless Drum, Spottail. (L. S. Caine gives 22 common names for this well-known fish.) *Color Plate 32*.

DISTRIBUTION: New York to Texas.

COLOR: May run lighter or darker, varying from grayish-silver with coppery tones on the back, to copper-red all over.

DISTINGUISHING CHARACTERS: The black spot at the tail base. Copper color. No scales on the dorsal rays. Long head. Outer teeth of the upper jaw are much enlarged.

SIZE: Commercially marketed at 5 pounds ("puppy drum"). Runs frequently to 15 and reaches over 75 pounds.

FOOD: Shrimps, crabs, mullet, menhaden, and other smaller fishes.

HABITS: Sandy shores. Schools. Inlets, channels between bars. Van Campen Heilner advises fishing close to the break on the bar. North of the Carolinas, June to October. In October also, large schools near shore in the Gulf of Mexico on their way to spawn in the mouths of the passes. Records have been caught off New

WHITING

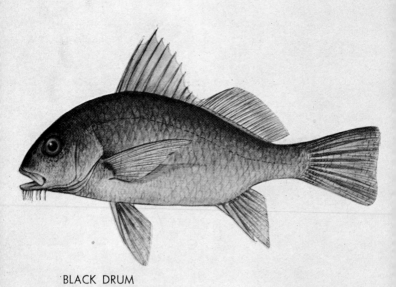

BLACK DRUM

PLATE 33

OCEAN WHITEFISH

ROCKFISH

PLATE 34

Inlet, New Jersey (September); Chincoteague, Virginia, and Titusville, Florida (June); Cape Hatteras, North Carolina (November).

Consult the local game warden if fishing for this in Texas waters.

Black Croaker   *Sciaena saturna* (Girard)

NAMES: Red Roncador, Chinese Croaker, Black Perch, Blue Bass, Black Bass.

DISTRIBUTION: North to Point Conception, California.

COLOR: Dusky dark blue on upper part of sides, and dusky silver below. The body has a coppery luster. Scales have dark dots. There may be a faint pale band from the middle of the dorsal-fin base to the lower edge of the body. Fins dark. A black blotch on the upper edge of the gill cover.

DISTINGUISHING CHARACTERS: The snout projects beyond the lower jaw. Pectoral fin is shorter than the head. The dorsal fin is deeply notched between spines and rays. The rays are closely scaled. A rather pointed nose and humped outline of head.

SIZE: Reaches about 15″.

FOOD: Fishes and crustaceans.

HABITS: Present all year.

Spotfin Croaker   *Roncador stearnsi* (Steindachner)

NAMES: Red Roncador, Black Croaker, Golden Croaker.

DISTRIBUTION: North to San Francisco, California.

COLOR: Bluish-steel or brilliant brassy above, silvery below. Wavy, dark, oblique lines on the body. Large, round, black spot on the base of the pectoral fin. Fins dusky.

DISTINGUISHING CHARACTERS: Black spot on pectoral base. Evenly rounded outline from tip of snout to beginning of the dorsal fin. Dorsal fin continuous but very deeply notched between the spines and the rays. Tail margin straight. The snout projects beyond the lower jaw. The pectoral fin is long. Scales on the rays of dorsal and anal fins.

SIZE: Reaches 5 or 6 pounds.

FOOD: Fishes, crustaceans.

HABITS: Inshore on sandy beaches and in surf.

Kingfish   *Genyonemus lineatus* (Ayres)

NAMES: White Croaker, Chenfish, Tomcod, Shiner, Herring, Carbinette, California Kingfish.

DISTRIBUTION: North to San Francisco, California.

COLOR: Silvered brownish above, shading into silvery white

below. Faint brown spots on the scales form oblique wavy lines above the lateral line. Fins yellowish. A black spot on the inner side of the pectoral, at base.

DISTINGUISHING CHARACTERS: Thirteen dorsal spines; 2 series of tiny barbels on sides of the lower jaw—none in its center. Scales have finely toothed edges. Snout beyond lower jaw. Second anal spine small and feeble. Scales on head and gill cover equal in size.

SIZE: Up to 1'.

FOOD: Crustaceans, fishes.

HABITS: Schools with the Queenfish and others.

Croaker *Micropogon undulatus* (Linnaeus)

NAMES: Corvina, Roncadina, Ronco, Crocus, Hardhead, Chut.

DISTRIBUTION: Cape Cod, Massachusetts, to Texas.

COLOR: Brassy, getting paler below. Sides above lateral line with short lines of dark spots. Some dark spots on upper fins.

DISTINGUISHING CHARACTERS: Minute barbels on sides of lower jaws. Middle rays of tail fin longer than the others. Outer teeth of the upper jaw enlarged. Dorsal strongly notched (to the base) between its spines and its rays. Mouth underslung.

SIZE: Averages about 1 pound but grows to 5 or more.

FOOD: Crustaceans, mollusks, smaller fishes.

HABITS: Generally common; most abundant from Maryland south. Bays, bayous, shallow water over grassy bottoms.

Yellowfin Croaker *Umbrina roncador* Jordan & Gilbert

NAMES: Yellow-finned Roncador, Yellow-tailed Croaker.

DISTRIBUTION: North to San Francisco, California.

COLOR: Metallic brassy and silvery reflections.

DISTINGUISHING CHARACTERS: Chin barbel. Second anal spine long and strong. *Color Plate 32.*

SIZE: Reaches a length of slightly over 1'.

HABITS: Common from San Diego, California, south, on shallow sandy shores.

Whiting *Menticirrhus saxatilis* (Bloch & Schneider)

NAMES: Northern Kingfish, Northern Whiting, Kingfish, Sea Mink, King Whiting, Sea Mullet. *Color Plate 33.*

DISTRIBUTION: Cape Ann, Massachusetts (straggling to Casco Bay, Maine), south to coasts of Florida, but more common north of Chesapeake Bay.

COLOR: Varies in tone from gray to black.

DISTINGUISHING CHARACTERS: Chin barbel. S-shaped margin

CABEZONE

PACIFIC CULTUS

PLATE 35

ATKA MACKEREL

BARRED PERCH

PLATE 36

of tail. Anal has one long spine. First dorsal spine prolonged into a filament.

SIZE: Averages 1 to 3 pounds; runs to 6.

FOOD: Shrimps, crabs, other crustaceans, small mollusks, fishes. Feeds close to the bottom.

HABITS: Schools over hard or sand bottoms near coasts. Replaced southward by the Southern Kingfish.

Southern Kingfish   *Menticirrhus americanus* (Linnaeus)

NAMES: Kingfish, Bermuda Whiting, Carolina Whiting, Silver Whiting, Surf Whiting, Sand Whiting, and most of the names used for the Whiting.

DISTRIBUTION: New Jersey to Texas, but not common north of Chesapeake Bay.

COLOR: Dull silvery with wide, dusky, oblique bars from ridge of back down and forward across the lateral line. Pectoral yellowish with dark tip.

DISTINGUISHING CHARACTERS: Range. Very much like the Whiting. Single weak anal spine. Chin barbel. Dorsal spine not prolonged as in the Whiting. Rayed dorsal long and low. S-shaped margin of tail fin.

SIZE: Averages below 1 pound, running up to 5.

FOOD: As that of the Whiting.

HABITS: Sandy coasts.

Black Drum   *Pogonias cromis* (Linnaeus)

NAMES: Drum, Sea Drum, Banded Drum, Gray Drum, Striped Drum. Its other names are confusing, and if possible it would be best to forget them. *Color Plate 33.*

DISTRIBUTION: Long Island, New York, to Texas.

COLOR: Ranges from dark gray to coppery.

DISTINGUISHING CHARACTERS: Van Campen Heilner describes this fish as "an oafish fellow with a beard, a hump on his back, stripes like a convict, and the fighting ability of a sack of potatoes." Barbels on the lower jaw. Throat teeth very large and blunt. Dorsal spines high. Long and very strong second anal spine.

SIZE: Runs over 140 pounds, but averages 3 to 6.

FOOD: Feeds on the bottom. Clams, oysters, shrimps, mollusks, fishes.

HABITS: Large schools in inlets, bays, and surf, and around pilings, etc.

THE BLANQUILLOS, ROCKFISHES, and SCULPINS are apt to be taken in the same places, and with much the same emotions by most anglers. They are usually thrown back and not mentioned. They are, however, pulled up very often and here included for recognition.

Ocean Whitefish   *Caulolatilus princeps* (Jenyns)

NAMES: Blanquillo, Whitefish. *Color Plate 34.*

DISTRIBUTION: North to Monterey, California; more common southward.

DISTINGUISHING CHARACTERS: The single dorsal is evenly high throughout and has 24 rays. There are two feeble anal spines and 23 rays. Very small scales. Small mouth and thick lips. No teeth on roof of mouth. Large canine teeth toward the back of the jaws.

SIZE: Reported as reaching 40″.

HABITS: A warm-water fish usually taken near the rocky islands off the coast.

Rockfish   Genus: *Sebastodes*

There are over fifty species of this Rockfish, and the majority of them are taken off the California coast. They run north to Puget Sound, Washington, and a number are found off Alaska. Many of them frequent very deep water. The one shown in the plate is the Red Rockfish, from Alaska. They are known by a variety of names and recognizable by:

A long, single, notched dorsal fin. Body covered with scales; 13 strong spines in the dorsal fin and 3 in the anal. A bony ridge just under the skin running back from the lower part of the eye. A square tail. Thick lips. *Color Plate 34.*

Cabezone   *Scorpaenichthys marmoratus* (Ayres)

The Cabezone is given here as an example of the scaleless sculpins of which there are a large number, easily recognizable by their reddish or greenish bodies, the absence of scales, and the flaps above the eyes.

NAMES: Marbled Sculpin, Blue Cod, Bullhead, Cabezon, Scaleless Sculpin, Sculpin. *Color Plate 35.*

These fishes run from San Diego, California, north. This one is one of the commonest of the shallow-water sculpins found along the West coast. It reaches a length of 2½′ and a weight of 20 to 25 pounds, but averages smaller. The color is highly variable. The head has bony ridges and flaps above and around the eyes.

THE GREENLINGS all have a bony support from the eye across the cheek, just under the skin; a large mouth; strong pointed teeth in the jaws and teeth on the roof of the mouth.

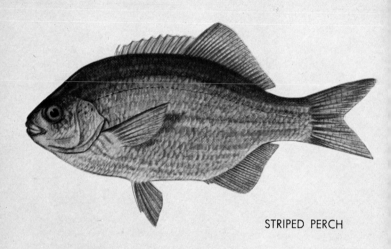

STRIPED PERCH

BLACKFISH

PLATE 37

HOGFISH

CALIFORNIA SHEEPSHEAD

PLATE 38

Pacific Cultus   *Ophiodon elongatus* (Girard)

NAMES: Ling, Cultus Cod. *Color Plate 35.*

DISTRIBUTION: Sitka, Alaska, south to Point Conception, California, and straggling southward.

COLOR: May be mottled grayish, or brown with small brown and yellow spots. In the dark specimens the flesh is green.

DISTINGUISHING CHARACTERS: No anal spines. A long dorsal fin with notch between spines and rays. No scales on the head.

SIZE: Runs to 4′ and 30 or 40 pounds.

HABITS: Abundant throughout its range.

California Sea Trout *Hexagrammos decagrammus* (Pallas)

NAMES: Rock Trout, Rockfish, Greenling, Boregat, Bodieron.

DISTRIBUTION: Point Conception, California, to Kodiak Island, Alaska.

COLOR: Grayish-brown, sometimes with blue or copper; males with light blue spots on head, lips, and upper sides. These spots in the female fish are brown.

DISTINGUISHING CHARACTERS: Anal spine, if present, is rudimentary. There is a deep notch between the spiny and the rayed dorsal. There are 5 lateral lines.

SIZE: Runs up to 18″.

FOOD: Crustaceans.

HABITS: More abundant in the southern part of its range.

Atka Mackerel   *Pleurogrammus monopterygius* (Pallas)

DISTRIBUTION: Aleutians, particularly Unalaska, Atka, and Attu; Pribilofs, Shumagins. *Color Plate 36.*

COLOR: Another phase is grayish.

DISTINGUISHING CHARACTERS: Long single dorsal fin without a notch between the spines and the rays. There are 5 lateral lines on each side. No anal spines.

SIZE: Averages slightly over 2 pounds; runs to slightly under 4.

FOOD: Crustaceans.

HABITS: Inshore in large schools, feeding among the kelp beds. April to July and straggling on into October.

THE SURF FISHES are a Pacific family which bear live young. They live in the surf and over sandy bottom in bays and are popular with many anglers. There are about 17 species, all looking much alike. The general characters are:

Rather deep body. No teeth on roof of the smallish mouth. Three anal spines; a continuous and rather long dorsal with as many as 11 spines. Both anal and dorsal fins are heavily scaled.

The tail fin is more or less forked. The fishes average in size between 6 and 8″ but are caught up to 1½′.

DISTRIBUTION: North to Alaska.

HABITS: Over sand and rock in surf or bays.

Following are some typical examples of the family. A number of additional surf fishes are listed and described in L. A. Walford's *Handbook of Commercial and Game Fishes of California,* 1931.

Barred Perch *Amphistichus argenteus* Agassiz

NAMES: Surf Perch, Silver Perch, Surf Fish. *Color Plate 36.*

DISTRIBUTION: San Diego, California, to Cape Flattery, Washington.

COLOR: Very metallic.

DISTINGUISHING CHARACTERS: Color pattern (see plate). Rays of the dorsal fin are a little higher than the spines.

Rainbow Perch *Hypsurus caryi* (Agassiz)

NAMES: Striped Perch, Bugara.

DISTRIBUTION: California coast, but most abundant north of Point Conception.

COLOR: Horizontal stripes of red, orange, and light blue on body, and streaks of orange and blue on the lower jaw, cheeks, breast, and belly. Bright light blue band around the eye and spots of light blue on the head. A black spot on the rayed dorsal. Anal and ventral fins mottled with orange, blue-tipped. Tail fin orange, with gray-dotted crossbars. Base of the pectoral orange edged with blue.

DISTINGUISHING CHARACTERS: The brilliant orange and blue coloring.

Striped Perch *Taeniotoca lateralis* (Agassiz)

NAMES: Blue Perch, Rainbow Perch, Squawfish, Striped Surf Fish. *Color Plate 37.*

DISTRIBUTION: San Diego, California, to Vancouver Island; rare south of Point Conception, California.

DISTINGUISHING CHARACTERS: The margin of the tail fin is concave, not forked. The rays of the dorsal fin much higher than the spines. Color.

SIZE: Averages 7″ or 8″; reaches 15″.

THE WRASSES are a group of fishes having in common: A terminal mouth. Front teeth of the jaws very strong canines, sometimes together at the base, but the separation evident (not fused as in the Parrotfishes). Throat teeth. A continuous dorsal fin. Anal with 2 to 6 spines (our examples have 3).

There are many species, but few are game fishes.

Blackfish or Tautog   *Tautoga onitis* (Linnaeus)

NAMES: Oysterfish. *Color Plate 37.*

DISTRIBUTION: New Brunswick to South Carolina.

DISTINGUISHING CHARACTERS: Sixteen dorsal spines. Two series of conical teeth in the jaws. Margin of the tail fin is straight with rounded corners.

SIZE: Reaches a weight of over 22 pounds, but averages under 10.

FOOD: Chiefly mollusks.

HABITS: Among rocks in 5 to 6 fathoms. Very abundant May to November. Goes offshore in winter.

Hogfish   *Lachnolaimus maximus* (Walbaum)

NAMES: Capitan, Perro Perro. *Color Plate 38.*

DISTRIBUTION: North to Key West, Florida.

COLOR: Varies. Sometimes entirely gray or entirely reddish-brown. Light or dark, depending on the bottom.

DISTINGUISHING CHARACTERS: Bright colors (see plate). The first three dorsal spines are prolonged into conspicuous streamers.

SIZE: Reaches 12 to 15 pounds.

FOOD: Feeds in the daytime on mollusks and crustaceans.

HABITS: Singly or two or three together. Rare about coral or bare sand; most common near sea fans.

California Sheepshead   *Pimelometopon pulcher* (Ayres)

NAMES: California Redfish, Fathead, Humpy. *Color Plate 38.*

DISTRIBUTION: North to Point Conception, California.

COLOR: Sometimes all black or dusky rose.

DISTINGUISHING CHARACTERS: Fat hump on male's forehead during breeding season. Large, forward-pointing canine teeth. Shape of tail margin. (See plate.)

SIZE: Reaches 15 pounds.

HABITS: An inshore fish.

Silver Hake   *Merluccius bilinearis* (Mitchill)

NAMES: New England Hake, Whiting. *Plate 39.*

DISTRIBUTION: Grand Banks south. Common Maryland to Nova Scotia.

COLOR: Dark brownish-gray. Lower sides and belly silvery. Inside of mouth dusky.

SILVER HAKE

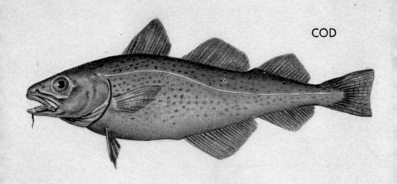
COD

PLATE 39

DISTINGUISHING CHARACTERS: Two dorsals, both without spines, the second much longer than the first. One anal, no spines. W-shaped ridges on top of the head.

SIZE: Averages about 14" long, but runs up to 2' and a weight of 8 pounds.

FOOD: Schooling fishes, squids, crustaceans.

HABITS: A migratory fish. Enormous schools. Sandy shores. Common in summer from western Nova Scotia to Cape Cod, Massachusetts, and the edge of the Continental Shelf off southern New England, and on Georges Bank. Inshore off southern New England in autumn.

The only Pacific hake is:

Hake   *Merluccius productus* (Ayres)

It is a blackish or iron-gray fish with silvery sides and a black mouth lining. It runs from Puget Sound, Washington, south. The W-shaped ridges are present but not as plain as in the Silver Hake.

Cod   *Gadus callarias* Linnaeus

NAMES: Rock Cod. *Plate 39.*

DISTRIBUTION: Cape Hatteras, North Carolina, to beyond our northern limits.

COLOR: Varies from reddish-brown to grayish-black on back and upper sides; shades into lighter tones on the sides and into white on the belly. Brown or yellowish dots on the sides; red or gray fins. The lateral line is always paler than the body color.

DISTINGUISHING CHARACTERS: Pale lateral line. Three dorsal fins; two anals; no spines. Single barbel below chin. Margin of tail fin square or very slightly concave.

SIZE: Reaches a weight of well over 200 pounds. Averages 10 to 12 pounds, and 25 on the banks.

FOOD: All invertebrates of suitable size, smaller fishes.

HABITS: Migratory both geographically and as to depth in the ocean. Nantucket shoals all year; most abundant spring to fall. Migrates to Rhode Island and then to North Carolina areas in fall and stays till May. Larger ones go into deeper water. Ranges from surface to 250 fathoms. Dr. W. C. Schroeder has made a very interesting report on the migrations (studied by tagging) of this fish in the *Bulletin of the Bureau of Fisheries,* Washington, 1930, XLVI.

POLLOCK

TOMCOD

PLATE 40

Tomcod   Genus: *Microgadus*

This fish, known also as Frostfish, is caught incidentally by anglers on both coasts and is a smaller edition of the Cod. The plate shows the Tomcod of the Atlantic, *Microgadus tomcod* (Walbaum). The margin of the tail is convex. The ventral fins extend into a long filament. The fish is olive or gray above, shading into yellowish or grayish below. Dorsal and tail fins are the color of the back; the anals lighter at the base. All the fins are mottled. *Plate 40.* The Pacific species strongly resembles this.

The Atlantic Tomcod runs from the Gulf of St. Lawrence to Virginia; the Pacific, from Monterey, California, to Unalaska.

Pollock   *Pollachius virens* (Linnaeus)

NAMES: Pollack, Coalfish, Boston Bluefish, Green Cod.

DISTRIBUTION: Nova Scotia to Virginia; rare south of Connecticut. *Plate 40.*

COLOR: Green, quite dark above and silvery green-gray below. The lateral line is lighter than the body tone. Ventral fins slightly pinkish; other fins olive. The anal is lighter at the base.

DISTINGUISHING CHARACTERS: Light lateral line. Large fishes usually have no barbel. Forked tail margin. Green color. Three dorsals and 2 anals; no spines.

SIZE: Averages 4 to 12 pounds; runs to about 35.

FOOD: Crustaceans, smaller schooling fishes.

HABITS: The schools are more abundant within 10 miles of land. Larger fishes are abundant in autumn and winter farther offshore; inshore in spring. A cold-water fish.

THE FLATFISHES comprise over 50 genera and 500 species, many of which are occasionally, and some very frequently, caught by anglers. They are unmistakable because they are flattened from side to side and the color and both eyes are on one side only.

Young flatfishes have normally placed eyes, but with growth one eye migrates over the top of the head and settles beside the other. At the same time the fish begins a one-sided life, the downside becoming white, and the topside possessing both eyes and, usually, all the color.

Winter Flounder
Pseudopleuronectes americanus (Walbaum)

NAMES: Flatfish. *Plate 41.*

DISTRIBUTION: Labrador to Cape Hatteras, North Carolina; abundant Massachusetts to New York.

COLOR: (upper side) Dark reddish-brown; sometimes a few reddish spots.

WINTER FLOUNDER

STARRY FLOUNDER

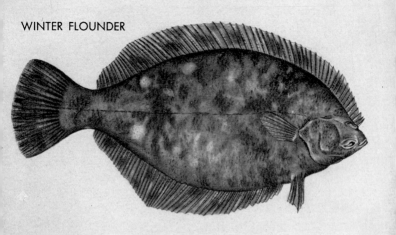

PLATE 41

DISTINGUISHING CHARACTERS: Eyes on the right side; small mouth; nearly, or entirely, one color on the upper side.

SIZE: Seldom larger than 5 pounds.

FOOD: Crabs, shellfish.

HABITS: A bottom fish; near shore late winter and early spring.

Summer Flounder   *Paralichthys dentatus* (Linnaeus)

NAMES: Fluke, Northern Flounder, Northern Fluke.

DISTRIBUTION: Cape Cod, Massachusetts, to Florida.

COLOR: (upper side) Light greenish-brown, mottled, and with many white spots on body and fins.

DISTINGUISHING CHARACTERS: Eyes on the left side; large mouth; spots.

SIZE: Two to 8 pounds; reaches over 19 pounds.

FOOD: Crabs, shrimps.

HABITS: Sandy bottoms; in bays.

Southern Flounder
Paralichthys lethostigmus Jordan & Gilbert

NAMES: Southern Fluke.

DISTRIBUTION: North to New York, but common southward and in the Gulf.

COLOR: Dark olive on the upper side.

DISTINGUISHING CHARACTERS: Dark color; otherwise as in the Summer Flounder.

Gulf Flounder   *Paralichthys albiguttus* Jordan & Gilbert

NAMES: Gulf Fluke.

The range within which this fish is common appears to be the Carolinas south to Florida and the Gulf. It is like the other fishes of the genus but characterized by a mottled gray or brown ground color with many pale spots. It runs small but reaches a length of slightly over 1'.

California Halibut   *Paralichthys californicus* (Ayres)

NAMES: Halibut, Chicken Halibut, Southern Halibut, Alabato.

DISTRIBUTION: San Francisco, California, south.

COLOR: (upper side) Greenish-brown; mottled.

DISTINGUISHING CHARACTERS: Lateral line arched in front. Pectoral fin on the eyed side shorter than the head. Small eyes.

SIZE: Reaches a weight of 60 pounds, but averages smaller.

HABITS: Present all year; especially abundant February to May.

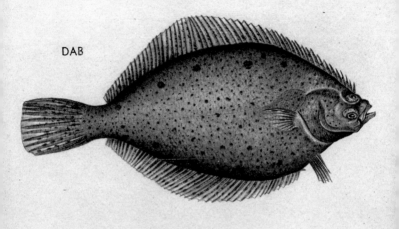

DAB

HALIBUT

PLATE 42

Starry Flounder *Platichthys stellatus* (Pallas)

NAMES: California Flounder. *Plate 41.*

DISTRIBUTION: Point Conception, California, north; abundant in Alaska.

COLOR: Very dark blotchy brown on the upper side. Alternating black and dull orange vertical bands on dorsal and anal fins and similar horizontal bands on tail.

DISTINGUISHING CHARACTERS: The dark bars on the fins. Star-shaped tubercles scattered all over the body and head. Small mouth; projecting lower jaw. Generally described as right-eyed, but averages 50% left-eyed in California, and 75% in Alaska.

SIZE: Reaches 20 pounds, but averages much less.

HABITS: Shallow water; sometimes ascends rivers.

Rusty Dab *Limanda ferruginea* (Storer)

DISTRIBUTION: New York south. *Plate 42.*

COLOR: (upper side) Greenish-brown. Body and fins covered with rusty red dots. Tail and edges of dorsal and anal fins on the blind side are yellow.

DISTINGUISHING CHARACTERS: Lateral line arched in front; small scales. Eyes on the right side and separated by a narrow ridge. A prominent humped nose. One anal spine.

Halibut *Hippoglossus hippoglossus* Linnaeus

DISTRIBUTION: Atlantic: New Jersey north to at least Latitude 64°. Pacific: San Francisco, California, north. *Plate 42.*

COLOR: Dark brown.

DISTINGUISHING CHARACTERS: Eyes on right side. The color.

SIZE: Known to weigh between 300 and 400 pounds and reported up to 700. Reaches a length of 7' to 8' and a width of 4'.

HABITS: Common in the northern part of its range and occasionally taken by sportsmen in British Columbia and Alaska.

FRESH-WATER FISHES

Anglers are again warned to consult local game wardens about licenses, seasons, sizes, and waters open to them. Most local tackle dealers have copies of the fishing laws available. These vary from district to district and from year to year.

It is particularly hard to choose from all the fresh-water fishes those that may be considered game. This is much more a local matter than is the case with salt-water fishes, as some fresh-water fishes are very sluggish in some localities or run small, or there are so many larger and gamier ones present that they are not considered game, whereas in other localities and under other conditions they are prized by anglers. Some also are extremely rare but gamy if an angler happens to hook into one.

The matter of common names is very confusing here as well as in the salt-water fishes—in fact, more so here. Every fresh-water fish appears to have about twenty or more common names. These have been listed over and over again; some have been included that are never known to be used; others have become misspelled out of recognition. Some of the states are making a great effort to standardize these names, and certainly they should receive full co-operation from angler and ichthyologist in this difficult task.

Bowfin   *Amia calva* Linnaeus

NAMES: Fresh-water Dogfish, Mudfish, Choupique, Grindle, Lawyer, Lake Lawyer, Cottonfish, Speckled Cat, Scaled Ling, Poisson de marais. *Plate 43.*

DISTRIBUTION: St. Lawrence-Champlain basin in Quebec and Vermont, southward, west of the Appalachians to Florida and Texas, and northward on the Atlantic slope to the Carolinas. Throughout the Great Lakes region but only in the drainage basin of Lake Superior in its outlet, St. Mary's River (C. L. Hubbs).

COLOR: Mottled olive; breeding male with black "eye spot" rimmed with orange at upper base of tail fin.

DISTINGUISHING CHARACTERS: Single long, low dorsal of uniform height; no spines. Short, round snout. Bony plate ("gular" plate) on throat between the branches of the lower jaw. Very soft flesh. General body contour.

SIZE: Reaches 2′ and 12 pounds.

FOOD: Mollusks, crustaceans, insects, other fishes.

HABITS: Sluggish water in weeds and mud in lakes, rivers, and swamps. Moves in groups particularly in the northern range in winter. Famous for nest-building habits and ability to survive in small amount of water. It has powerful teeth and is a voracious, pugnacious fish and a strong fighter.

Mooneye   *Hiodon tergisus* LeSueur

NAMES: White Shad, Toothed Herring, White-eyed Mooneye.

DISTRIBUTION: Mississippi Valley and the Great Lakes north to southern Manitoba. *Plate 43.*

COLOR: Olive on the back and upper sides; bright iridescent silvery below. Fins light.

DISTINGUISHING CHARACTERS: Herring-like, but has a lateral line and strong, wide-spaced teeth. Short, spineless dorsal fin begins above anal fin. Very large eye.

SIZE: About 1′ or less.

FOOD: Minnows, mollusks, insects, worms.

HABITS: Abundant in Lake Erie and the Ohio River. Open waters of large lakes and streams, but small schools often come into creeks or close to shore at night.

Goldeye   *Hiodon alosoides* (Rafinesque)

NAMES: Gold-eyed Mooneye, Northern Mooneye, Toothed Herring, Wap, La Quesche, Naccaysh.

DISTRIBUTION: Ohio River northwest to Manitoba and Saskatchewan.

BOWFIN

PLATE 43

MOONEYE

COLOR: Bluish above; goldish-silvery below, with pearly iridescence toward the tail.

DISTINGUISHING CHARACTERS: Shorter dorsal than the Mooneye, which it resembles. Body of adult deep and keeled along the lower edge.

SIZE: Eight to 12″.

FOOD: Insects, mollusks, minnows.

HABITS: More abundant in Canada. More common in swift open water.

TROUTS AND SALMONS: Salmon go from the sea to fresh water to spawn. The urge to go upstream for this purpose is shared by the Trouts, but as they live in fresh water anyway, the journey is not so remarkable. Northward there is a tendency for these fishes to become marine and southward to become fresh-water.

Pacific Salmon die after spawning as a rule, but Atlantic Salmon, Trout and Steelhead do not.

Pacific salmons spawn from March to December, depending upon the species. Steelhead spawn in autumn, winter, or early spring; Cut-throat in spring, and Atlantic Salmon, Eastern Brook Trout, Dolly Varden, Lake Trout, and Brown Trout in autumn. Breeding male fish are highly colored, usually with a lot of red; the upper jaw is humped, and in the Pacific salmons both jaws are hooked. Salmons and trouts in breeding condition have two hard ridges on the under side of the belly.

A very interesting paper on this subject is "The Breeding Habits of Salmon and Trout," by L. P. Schultz (*Smithsonian Report for 1937*, Washington, D.C.).

There are a great many species and local varieties of trout—far too many to cover in this short book. Not all of them are game fish. A well-illustrated complete book on this subject would be a boon to anglers.

Individual trout of the same species vary greatly in color and size, depending on locality and conditions. Unless two kinds of trout remain consistently different in identical conditions, it is not at all certain that they are really two kinds. To add to the confusion, trouts are known to interbreed; and furthermore, in the past, hatcheries sometimes finding females of one kind of trout ready to spawn but males not ready, have simply used males of another kind, thus creating some hybrid offspring with which waters have been stocked.

Fortunately, local anglers are usually well informed about their own trouts and also about what has been stocked. It is futile to attempt a full distinguishing key to these fishes, and one must depend on local fishermen who know the fish well by sight. There are dozens of local varieties, some not at all well known to the general angling public, and others like the Sunapee Trout, the Oquassa Trout, the Lake Tahoe Trout, etc., very well known. It is only possible here to give an indication of the varieties by choosing some of the most widely varied. Many of the local fish-and-game commissions have published on their own trouts. I would particularly recommend to anglers J. R. Dymond's *The Trout and Other Game Fishes of British Columbia,* published by the Biological Board of Canada, Ottawa, 1932.

There are many large and fine color plates in parts 1 and 2 of W. C. Kendall's *The Fisheries of New England,* published from 1914 to 1927 by the Boston Society of Natural History (the text is technical).

CONDENSED KEY TO THE GROUPS

ATLANTIC SALMON .... *Salmo*	Anal fin has 9 rays. Teeth on roof of mouth few and easily lost. No spots on tail fin.
RAINBOW (STEELHEAD) TROUT *Salmo*	Anal has 10 to 13 rays. Teeth on roof of mouth many and strong. Tail fin spotted. No red under lower jaw; 130–35 scales in longitudinal row.
CUT-THROAT TROUT .... *Salmo*	As in Rainbow, except: red under lower jaw; more than 150 scales.
LAKE TROUT .... *Cristivomer*	Anal has 10 to 13 rays. Teeth on roof of mouth on an elevated crest. Red or pale spots on body. Tail strongly forked. Teeth on base of tongue.
BROOK TROUT .... *Salvelinus*	Anal has 10 to 13 rays. No teeth on root of tongue. Red or pink spots on sides; back with dark mottlings; lower fins with light edges; tail square or only slightly forked.
DOLLY VARDEN .... *Salvelinus*	As in Brook, except: back not mottled.
PACIFIC SALMON .... *Oncorhynchus*	Anal with 14 to 17 rays.

Dog Salmon *Oncorhynchus keta* (Walbaum)

NAMES: Dog, Hayko, Chum Salmon, Le Kai Salmon, Calico Salmon. *Color Plate 44.*

DISTRIBUTION: Sacramento River, California, to Bering Strait.

COLOR: Silvery, with or without black specks. Breeding males brick-red to blackish-red, with very much distorted jaws.

DISTINGUISHING CHARACTERS: See key for Pacific Salmon (page 105). General shape rather like that of the Chinook Salmon, but the head is longer and more pikelike and the end of the upper jawbone reaches considerably beyond a vertical dropped from the back of the eye.

SIZE: Rarely exceeds 10 pounds, but has been caught at 20.

FOOD: Insects, crustaceans, some small fishes.

HABITS: Spawns only a short distance above salt water. Migrates to sea very young.

Blueback Salmon *Oncorhynchus nerka* (Walbaum)

NAMES: Sockeye, Sockeye Salmon, Blueback, Red Salmon, Redfish, Saweye, Sukkegh Salmon, Fraser River Salmon, Nerka, Krasnaya Ryba (Russian for red fish). *Color Plate 44.*

DISTRIBUTION: Oregon to Alaska; occasionally straggles farther north.

COLOR: When spawning in the fall, they usually turn bright red with a greenish head.

SIZE: Seldom over 6 pounds; maximum 12.

FOOD: Insects, crustaceans, sometimes fishes.

HABITS: Spawns far upstream.

Kokanee *Oncorhynchus nerka kennerlyi* (Suckley)

NAMES: Kikanniny, Little Redfish, Kennerly's Salmon, Kennerly's Trout, Silver Salmon.

This fish is found from Idaho and Oregon to Alaska. It runs small, usually under a pound. It is bright silver-bluish except in breeding season, when it becomes spotted above and various dark colors. Like other Pacific salmons, it dies after spawning. These fish mature at half a pound and would seem to be a dwarfed form.

Chinook Salmon *Oncorhynchus tschawytscha* (Walbaum)

NAMES: King Salmon, Quinnat Salmon, Columbia River Salmon, Tyee, Spring Salmon, Blackmouth Salmon, Sacramento River Salmon, Tchaviche, Tschawytscha. *Color Plate 45.*

The Tyee Club has an arbitrarily established low limit of 30 pounds as a Tyee; anything below that is a Spring.

DISTRIBUTION: California to Alaska, especially in Sacramento, Klamath, and Columbia rivers. Also introduced into a few New England lakes.

COLOR: Flesh is not as red as that of the Silver Salmon. Distorted spawning males are muddy dark red, almost black.

DISTINGUISHING CHARACTERS: Anal has 14 to 17 rays. Teeth on roof of mouth very small, and absent in the male fish. Robust body. Tail strongly forked. Eye small. Runs large.

SIZE: Up to 100 pounds; runs smaller in the southern part of its range.

FOOD: As in other salmons.

HABITS: Spawns chiefly in the larger streams and goes hundreds of miles up. Found at considerable depths in salt water, but also along edges of bars.

Silver Salmon   *Oncorhynchus kisutch* (Walbaum)

NAMES: Coho Salmon, Hoopid, Kisutch, Silversides, Skowitz, Quisutch, White Salmon, Bielaya Ryba (Russian for white fish), Pacific Salmon, Arctic Trout. *Color Plate 45.*

DISTRIBUTION: Monterey Bay, California, to Alaska.

COLOR: Sometimes obscure spots on back and dorsal fin; males red during spawning season.

DISTINGUISHING CHARACTERS: Anal has 14 to 17 rays; end of upper jawbone reaches slightly beyond a vertical from the back of the eye. No spots on head or tail. Only two or three very small teeth on the roof of the mouth. Tail strongly forked.

SIZE: Maximum about 15 pounds; averages 3 to 8.

HABITS: Goes into fresh water to spawn in the lower tributaries and dies after spawning. Abundant in Puget Sound and in Alaska.

Humpback Salmon   *Oncorhynchus gorbuscha* (Walbaum)

NAMES: Humpback, Pink Salmon, Dog Salmon, Haddo, Holia, Gorbusha. *Color Plate 46.*

DISTRIBUTION: San Diego region, California, to Alaska.

COLOR: Spawning males are reddish or blotched with brown.

DISTINGUISHING CHARACTERS: Fine small scales, more than 200 in horizontal row. Black spots on tail. Male's back very distinctly humped in spawning season.

SIZE: Averages 3 to 5 pounds; rarely over 7. The smallest of the Pacific salmons.

FOOD: Chiefly insects.

HABITS: The least migratory of the Pacific salmons, spawning only a few miles above sea water. More plentiful in the northern part of its range; not very common.

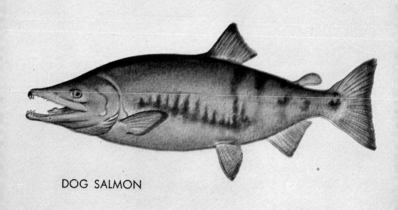

DOG SALMON

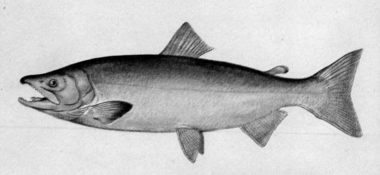

BLUEBACK SALMON

PLATE 44

CHINOOK SALMON

SILVER SALMON

PLATE 45

Rainbow Trout or Steelhead *Salmo gairdnerii* Richardson

So far, I find less reason for considering these as two different fishes than for considering them two different color phases of the same fish. Until something is proven otherwise, I suggest that anglers consider the Rainbow Trout and the Steelhead two different names of the same fish.

As most salmons or trouts take on silvery color when in the sea (this is not confined to the Rainbow), I would also suggest that we abandon the name Steelhead for any other of the trouts or salmons.

NAMES: Steelhead Trout, Steelhead Salmon, Hardhead, Salmon Trout. *Color Plate 46.*

DISTRIBUTION: Western North America from San Diego region to Alaska. Eastern and Central North America: has been widely introduced from Georgia north and west.

COLOR: Varies from one stream to another in fresh water. The plate shows the "Rainbow" phase from fresh water. The fish in salt water becomes silvery, with a bluish or greenish back; usually a few small dark dots above the lateral line and on the tail and dorsal fins. The lower fins are either dusky or whitish.

DISTINGUISHING CHARACTERS: The anal fin has from 10 to 14 rays; zigzag rows of teeth on the roof of the mouth; no red under the lower jaw; usually less than 150 scales in a lengthwise row. Breeding males bright red.

SIZE: Rainbows run much heavier than Cut-throats of the same length. An 18″ to 22″ fish may weigh from 2 to over 4¼ pounds; a 30″ to 34″ fish may weigh from 10 to 12 pounds. Averages 2 to 8 pounds and is reported to reach 40.

FOOD: Insects, crustaceans, worms, smaller fishes.

HABITS: If resident in salt water, goes upstream to spawn, but these excursions are not limited to spawning time. Can stand warmer and more quiet waters than the Brook Trout. Does not die after spawning.

NOTE: The fresh-water phase of this trout is geographically widespread and has acquired many different names in various localities. There are probably also slight geographical differences in the fish, such as scale count. Some of the best-known local fishes are the Klamath River, McCloud River, Kern River, the Rose, the San Bernardino, the Eagle Lakes, the Emerald, and the Silver Trout of Tahoe. There are many others.

Kamloops Trout *Salmo kamloops* Jordan

NOTE: This is sometimes included as a variety of the Rainbow.
NAMES: Stit-tse. *Color Plate 47.*

Distribution: Lakes tributary to the Fraser and Upper Columbia rivers. Stocked elsewhere.

Color: Varies greatly with environment. May be heavily spotted and greenish (shallow water); lightly speckled bluish, or silvery (larger fish); laterally banded with red, or dark-colored (spawning). The dark flecks are generally all above the lateral line except near the tail, and the lower sides are apt to be very silvery.

Distinguishing Characters: General shape is similar to that of the Steelhead, but the head of the Kamloops is larger.

Food: Insects, crayfish.

Size: Varies with the amount of available food. Said to reach 40 lbs.

Habits: Streams and lakes, mouths of streams flowing into larger bodies of water.

A geographical variety is the Mountain Kamloops, found in small lakes in high altitudes.

Atlantic Salmon   *Salmo salar* Linnaeus

Names: Kennebec Salmon, Salmon. *Color Plate 47.*

Distribution: Cape Cod, Massachusetts, north; sometimes straggles south as far as the Delaware River. In the ocean, its exact range has not been determined, but it has been taken from Delaware to Labrador.

Color and Distinguishing Characters: Black X-shaped and round spots. The sea-run fish is steel blue and silver with spots; the fresh-water fish is flushed with reddish. Anals and ventrals are white, the other fins dusky.

Size: Averages 10 to 20 pounds or less, depending on locality. Runs to over 80.

Food: Crustaceans, herring, and other small fishes; capelin, sand eels. Seldom eats in fresh water.

Habits: Ascends rivers to spawn. May survive three spawnings.

Landlocked Salmon   *Salmo salar sebago* Girard

This is a famous landlocked form of the Atlantic Salmon.

Names: Sebago Salmon, Sebago Trout, Schoodic Salmon, Lake Salmon. *Color Plate 48.*

Distribution: Maine north to Labrador.

Color: Varies from black to blue-green on back; rest of body whitish-silver. Black spots, irregularly double-X-shaped on upper part of body.

Distinguishing Characters: Shape of the spots. Larger eye, longer fins, and larger scales than the sea-run Atlantic Salmon.

Size: Averages 10 pounds; runs to over 35.

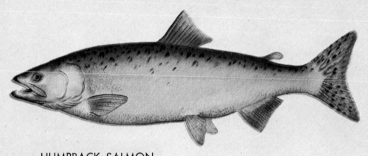

HUMPBACK SALMON

RAINBOW TROUT

PLATE 46

KAMLOOPS TROUT

ATLANTIC SALMON

PLATE 47

Food: Smelts and occasionally other fishes; insects.

Habits: Lakes where smelts are available. This landlocked form goes upstream from its lakes to spawn.

The Ouananiche, *Salmo salar ouananiche* McCarthy, is a Canadian Landlocked Salmon in the Upper Saguenay and tributaries, and rivers flowing into the Gulf of St. Lawrence. It differs from the Landlocked Salmon by its more northern distribution and smaller size, which averages 2 or 3 pounds, and seldom is as much as 8.

Brown and Loch Leven Trout   *Salmo trutta* Linnaeus

These two trouts, both natives of Europe, were introduced long ago into North America. They were crossbred by fish culturists until a clear strain of either has almost completely vanished.

Names: English Brown Trout, German Brown Trout, von Behr Trout, European Brown Trout, European Trout.

Distribution: California north. Georgia north.

Color: Varies considerably. *Color Plate 48.*

Distinguishing Characters: Red spots on side surrounded by light rings. Rather large scales. Large adipose fin.

Size: Often 7 or 8 pounds and runs to over 15 in our waters. (See record, page 174.)

Habits: Can live in warmer water than the Brook Trout. Very widely and successfully planted.

Cut-throat Trout   *Salmo clarkii* Richardson

Names: Native Trout, Black-spotted Trout, Colorado River Trout, and other names applying to localities. *Color Plate 49.*

Distribution: California to Alaska.

Color: Varies with locality. May run very dark; sometimes there are small golden spots on the body or large black spots on body and all fins; sometimes the ground color is yellowish-pink with a pinkish longitudinal stripe, sometimes with a purplish stripe. Occasionally it is very much like a sea-run Rainbow. There is a red gash under the lower jaw.

Distinguishing Characters: Red mark or blotch under lower jaw. Spots on jaws. Scales 160 to 200 in a horizontal row. Small teeth on base of the tongue.

Size, Food, Habits: As in other trouts. The record for Cut-throat is 41 pounds. There are numerous varieties of this fish from coastal localities to a height of 10,000 feet. Some are rarely taken and others well known. For these varieties, the angler is advised to consult the Division of Fish and Game of the state of California, San Francisco. They are practically impossible to differentiate except by actual specimens.

Lake Tahoe Cut-throat
Salmo clarkii henshawi Gill & Jordan

NAMES: Lake Tahoe Trout, Silver Trout of Lake Tahoe, Yellow-finned Trout of Lake Tahoe, Black-spotted Trout.

DISTRIBUTION: Lake Tahoe and the waters of the Truckee system.

COLOR: Varies with the stream. In deep water this fish is large and silvery with elongated dark spots. There may also be small round golden spots or many black spots on the body. It may run very dark. The spawning males are dark yellowish with a broad pinkish stripe; the base of the pectorals, two streaks under the lower jaw, and the tip of the tongue are bright red. Females are lighter in tone.

Piute Trout
Salmo clarkii seliniris Snyder

This, according to J. Snyder, is "an isolated variant of the Tahoe Cut-throat Trout." Anglers should consult local game wardens for the laws concerning this protected fish.

DISTRIBUTION: Native only in small streams of Fish Valley (Alpine County east of the Sierra Divide). Planted near Lake Tahoe. *Color Plate 49.*

COLOR: Snyder says that "no two observers agree on the colors . . . which seemingly come and go with every changing whim of the fish."

DISTINGUISHING CHARACTERS: Locality. Long, slender body and fragile fins.

Lake Trout
Cristivomer namaycush (Walbaum)

NAMES: Great Lake Trout, Mackinaw Trout, Salmon Trout, Namaycush, Longue, Togue, Forktail Trout, Lunge, Laker.

DISTRIBUTION: Northern New York, north and west to the Great Lakes and north, and from that basin north to Alaska.

COLOR: Varies with age, sex, season, food, and nature of water. Sometimes runs very dark. *Color Plate 50.*

DISTINGUISHING CHARACTERS: Teeth on roof of mouth are on a crest. Teeth on root of tongue. Pale spots. Forked tail.

SIZE: Averages 9 pounds or less; 20 is large but not uncommon; said to run over 100.

FOOD: Goatlike in appetite—fishes, such as smelts, eels; birds; leaves; trash.

HABITS: Deep cool water, usually the larger lakes; comes to surface to sun and inshore at times for food, and in the fall for spawning. Not very apt to go into salt water.

LANDLOCKED SALMON

BROWN TROUT

PLATE 48

CUT-THROAT TROUT

PIUTE TROUT

PLATE 49

Brook Trout   *Salvelinus fontinalis* (Mitchill)

NAMES: Eastern Brook Trout, Speckled Trout, Native Trout, Mountain Trout, Squaretail. *Color Plate 50.*

DISTRIBUTION: Georgia north to Labrador and west to Saskatchewan. Not native west of the Mississippi except in Minnesota and Iowa; introduced in the West and running from cold mountain waters of California north to British Columbia.

COLOR: Runs from very light to very dark.

DISTINGUISHING CHARACTERS: Square tail. Spots and mottlings. White-edged fins and reddish lower fins. Minute scales. No teeth on base of tongue.

SIZE: Rarely over 9 pounds; usually from 2 to 5. Record is over 14.

FOOD: Varies with locality: insects, mollusks, crustaceans, fishes.

HABITS: A Northern fish, usually in clear cold water; for instance, spring-fed pools, brooks, etc. Goes upstream into shallower water to spawn. Goes into the sea in the north. Breeding habits also vary. Some spawn upstream; others in shallower places in lakes.

Dolly Varden   *Salvelinus malma* (Walbaum)

NAMES: Bull Trout, Western Charr, Malma, Oregon Charr, Red-spotted Trout, Golet. *Color Plate 51.*

DISTRIBUTION: Native northern California (not common) to Alaska. Plentiful in British Columbia and north. Columbia River basin to Idaho and Montana.

COLOR: Varies in intensity of color. Sea-run specimens are silvery, with very pale spots or none, and white-laced fins; no red.

DISTINGUISHING CHARACTERS: Resembles the Brook Trout but is slenderer and without black markings. Dark yellow or orange spots in some specimens. Forked caudal.

SIZE: In creeks up to 2 pounds; in lakes and rivers runs up to over 20.

FOOD: Insects, any animal life available, young of other fishes, other trout.

HABITS: Abundant in streams and lakes in the north of its range; enters the sea. Very destructive to young and eggs of other fishes of its family. It has become landlocked in various lakes and is there known under various local names—usually "Trout" preceded by the name of the lake.

Golden Trout   *Salmo agua-bonita* Jordan

This is probably the same as the fish called *Salmo roosevelti.*

Distribution: Native to the high Sierras, at 10,000 feet or over, but introduced in Kern River, California, and tributaries.

Color: Varies somewhat with locality but always very brilliant. *Color Plate 51.*

Distinguishing Characters: Locality. Brilliant color, with much orange and yellow. Small scales.

Size: Rarely over 1 pound.

Food: Presumably insects. Stomach contents do not seem to have been examined.

Habits: High, clear brooks and lakes. Thrives very high.

THE WHITEFISHES: Only a very few of this numerous family can possibly be considered game fishes. Any attempt to go into local subspecies and varieties would be as utterly confusing to the angler as it has been and still is to many ichthyologists.

The fishes are difficult to distinguish, even technically, but local commercial fishermen in many localities are fortunate enough to know them by sight, although their identifications cannot always be completely depended upon, as a commercial catch under one name may include more than one kind.

I shall attempt to deal only with the three or four known to take the hook, but the characteristics of these should help identification of the genus at least, should any others be pulled up. Consult the plate for the difference in the appearance of the jaws. All have adipose fins, and the three here discussed develop small tubercles, known as "pearl organs," during the breeding season.

Dr. Walter Koelz has made a detailed study of this family, and the angler will find much of the less technical parts of two of his papers, as well as the plates, of interest and help. ("Coregonid Fishes of the Great Lakes," *Bureau of Fisheries Document* ⚡1048, Washington, 1929; and "The Coregonid Fishes of North-eastern America," *Papers of the Michigan Academy of Sciences, Arts & Letters,* Volume XIII, 1931.)

Lake Herring   *Leucichthys artedi* (LeSueur)

This genus has numerous local varieties.

Names: Cisco, Blueback, and numerous local names.

Distribution: Lakes from New York to Canada, and to the Great Lakes and Saskatchewan.

Color: Varies with locality. Pea green or blue-green above and halfway to lateral line; iridescent silvery below. Upper fins dusky; lower fins light. *Plate 52.*

Distinguishing Characters: Two flaps of membrane between the openings of each nostril. Teeth on the tongue. Mouth

LAKE TROUT

BROOK TROUT

PLATE 50

DOLLY VARDEN

GOLDEN TROUT

PLATE 51

(see plate). Pearl organs of uniform thickness present on head and sides of breeding males. There may be weak teeth in the jaws, or none.

SIZE: Usually under 2 pounds; reported to reach 6.

FOOD: Crustaceans, insects.

HABITS: Shallow water, feeding chiefly close to bottom. Schools inshore and offshore. In some lakes runs deeper than in others.

The Tullibee and other fishes local to certain lakes are varieties of this fish.

Whitefish   *Coregonus clupeaformis* (Mitchill)

Also known widely as the Lake Whitefish. Its appearance differs slightly in different bodies of water, and there are many very localized names. *Plate 52.*

DISTRIBUTION: New York and the Great Lakes.

COLOR: Varies with locality. Usually pale green on back and upper sides, shading into bluish-silvery with purple iridescence; sometimes many small dots on the head and fins. Fins whitish.

DISTINGUISHING CHARACTERS: Two flaps of membrane between the two openings of each nostril. Teeth on the tongue. Mouth (see plate). Pearl organs on head and sides of breeding males and also breeding females. These are much thicker in the middle. There may be weak teeth in the jaws, or none.

SIZE: This is the largest of the Whitefish family. It has been known to reach a weight of 26 pounds. A few of 8 to 10 pounds are taken each year, but it averages less.

FOOD: Mollusks, insects, fish.

HABITS: Schools come close to the shores of lakes or reefs around islands to spawn. Distance from shore depends upon season. Abundant.

Pilot   *Prosopium quadrilaterale* (Richardson)

NAMES: Menominee, Menominee Whitefish, Round Whitefish, Frostfish, Cisco, Grayback, Lake Minnow. *Plate 52.*

DISTRIBUTION: New York northward; west to the Great Lakes and north.

COLOR: Varies with locality. Top and upper sides brown or bronze, tinged with greenish. On sides the brown color is overlaid with silver and has a purplish tinge. Dorsal fin and portion of the tail brown. Sometimes there are bright pink splotches on the other fins.

DISTINGUISHING CHARACTERS: A single flap of membrane between the two openings of each nostril. No teeth on tongue

LAKE HERRING

WHITEFISH

PILOT

PLATE 52

or in jaws. Mouth (see plate). A short, heavy keel on top of the head between the eyes. Pearl organs on sides only in both sexes at breeding time.

SIZE: Maximum 5 pounds; averages 2 or less.

FOOD: Mollusks, insects, and probably spawn of other fishes.

HABITS: Schools move in and off shore.

Among the varieties of this fish well known to anglers are the Oregon Whitefish and the Mountain Whitefish.

Arctic Grayling   *Thymallus signifer* (Richardson)

NAMES: Alaska Grayling, American Grayling, Poisson Bleu.

DISTRIBUTION: McKenzie and Yukon rivers, British Columbia, Northwestern Territory, Alaska. *Plate 53.*

COLOR: Back dark blue; sides blotchy purple-gray. A few—about 18—well-spaced dark dots forward on the sides of the body. A blue mark on each side of the lower jaw. Dorsal fin dark gray with pale blotches, rows of dark blue spots, and a red edge. Lower fins with purplish and whitish streaks.

DISTINGUISHING CHARACTERS: The high, narrow dorsal fin (*see Plate 53*). Small mouth. Weak teeth.

American Grayling   *Thymallus signifer tricolor* Cope

NAMES: Michigan Grayling, Montana Grayling.

DISTRIBUTION: Upper Missouri basin above the Great Falls. Stocked in Michigan. Absent from the Great Lakes basin.

COLOR: Purplish-gray and silvery. Head blue and bronze. Small dark spots on body. Lower part of dorsal fin with alternating lines of dusky and rose; upper part of dorsal dotted with red or purple spots surrounded by bright green. Other fins brownish except for a blue area on the tip of the pectorals and some streaks of pink.

DISTINGUISHING CHARACTERS: The long, high, brilliantly colored dorsal fin.

SIZE: Averages from 1 to 2 pounds.

FOOD: Insects.

HABITS: Clear cold streams. The fish sometimes separated in angling books and called the Montana Grayling is technically not separable from this. It is a slightly less vivid color phase.

THE PIKES are long-bodied fishes with long, flat, duck-billed jaws and short, very similar dorsal and anal fins placed far back toward the tail and opposite each other.

Whole of gill cover, and usually whole cheek, scaled........
    Pickerel

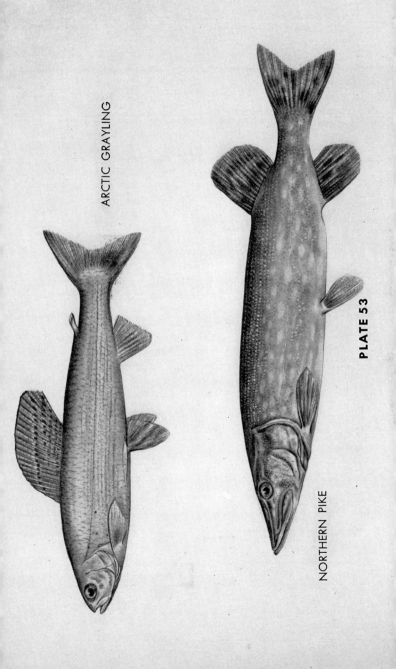

ARCTIC GRAYLING

NORTHERN PIKE

PLATE 53

Upper half of gill cover, and usually whole cheek, scaled
........Pike
Upper half of gill cover, and usually one half cheek, scaled
........Muskellunge

Northern Pike   *Esox lucius* Linnaeus

NAMES: American Pike, Common Pike, Great Northern Pike, Great Lakes Pike, Grass Pike, Pickerel, Great Northern Pickerel, Snake, Jackfish. (Numerous other names are listed by Weed in *Field Museum Zool. Leaflet Number 9*, 1927, pp. 1–52.)

DISTRIBUTION: Eastern New York, northern New England, Canada from east to west (rare in British Columbia), Alaska, Ohio Valley, Great Lakes, Missouri, Nebraska. *Plate 53.*

COLOR: Usually olive, shading into yellowish or whitish on belly. Short, light, barlike spots on body. Some dark spots on the fins. Eddy and Surber (*Northern Game Fishes,* 1943) report a Minnesotan variety, the Silver Muskellunge, as silvery or gray with black-speckled fins.

DISTINGUISHING CHARACTERS: Lower half of gill cover without scales. Large pores on head and lower jaw.

SIZE: Usually over 1′. Runs to over 4′ and 50 pounds.

FOOD: Fishes, including its own kind; insects; leeches. Eats enormously.

HABITS: Sluggish streams and shallow, weedy places in lakes; also cold, clear, rocky waters.

Barred Pickerel   *Esox americanus* Gmelin

NAMES: Bulldog Pickerel, Pickerel, Pike. *Plate 54.*

DISTRIBUTION: Maine to Florida and Alabama; east of the Allegheny Mountains.

COLOR: Dusky green; black bar below eye and curved dark bars on sides.

DISTINGUISHING CHARACTERS: Gill cover, and usually whole cheek, entirely scaled.

SIZE: Runs small; seldom over 1′ and 1 pound.

FOOD: Small fishes.

HABITS: Lowland streams; sometimes far up small brooks; swamps.

Mud Pickerel   *Esox vermiculatus* LeSueur

NAMES: Grass Pike.

This is a small pickerel, rarely running over 1′ and not ordinarily treated as a game fish. It is distributed in the Gulf States, the Ohio Valley, Lower Mississippi drainage, and into

BARRED PICKEREL

EASTERN
PICKEREL

PLATE 54

Ontario. The whole of the gill cover is scaled; the body is green, marked with wavy dark lines.

Eastern Pickerel
Esox niger LeSueur

(Also listed in many books as *Esox reticulatus.*)

NAMES: Chain Pickerel, Eastern Pike, Green Pike, Jack, True Pickerel, Duck-billed Pike, Lake Pickerel, Pond Pickerel, Grass Pickerel, Chain Pike. *Plate 54.*

DISTRIBUTION: New England to Florida and southwest to Texas. Abundant everywhere east and south of the Allegheny Mountains.

COLOR: Green, tinged with gold; lighter on lower part of body. Dark, chainlike network of interrupted lines on the sides. Dark bars behind the eyes. Fins without markings.

DISTINGUISHING CHARACTERS: Whole of gill cover scaled. Network of dark lines on sides of body.

SIZE: Averages about 2′; runs to 3′ or 4′ and over 10 pounds.

FOOD: Smaller fishes, frogs. Very greedy.

HABITS: Clear, grassy lakes and ponds and the quiet reaches of Southern streams. Often caught by anglers fishing for bass.

Muskellunge
Esox masquinongy Mitchill

NAMES: Various spellings of the name Muskellunge, Musky, Great Muskellunge, Great Pike. *Plate 55.*

DISTRIBUTION: Great Lakes region north to Canada; Upper Mississippi Valley northward.

COLOR: Green or greenish-brown or gray; lighter below. Dark spots and marks on the body and fins.

DISTINGUISHING CHARACTERS: No scales on the lower half of the gill cover. Markings dark.

SIZE: Up to more than 60 pounds.

FOOD: Fishes, frogs, snakes.

HABITS: Solitary in cool, clear, weedy water of lakes and quiet reaches of rivers.

Chautauqua Muskellunge
Esox masquinongy ohiensis Kirtland

A subspecies present in the Ohio River system; Chautauqua Lake, New York; Lake Ontario, and the St. Lawrence River.

NAMES: Ohio Muskellunge, Barred Muskellunge, Ohio River Pike, Allegheny River Pike, Jack, Pike. *Plate 55.*

This fish is marked with dark spots which form indefinite crossbars on the sides.

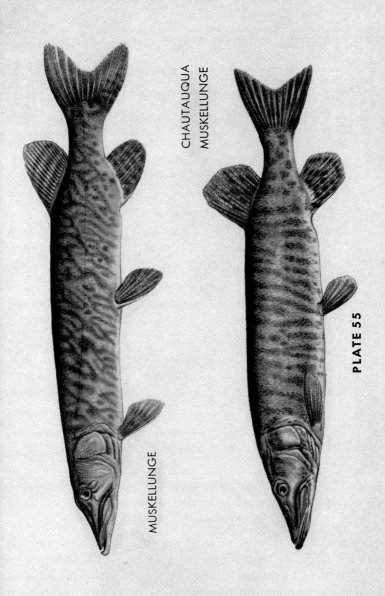

MUSKELLUNGE

CHAUTAUQUA
MUSKELLUNGE

PLATE 55

Northern Muskellunge
Esox masquinongy immaculatus Garrard

NAMES: Unspotted Muskellunge, Wisconsin Muskellunge, Tiger Muskellunge, Barred Muskellunge.

Another subspecies of the Muskellunge, found in lakes of Wisconsin and Minnesota. The body is apt to be more or less silvery, without spots, but with indistinct crossbands.

Troutperch   *Percopsis omiscomaycus* (Walbaum)

Opinions differ as to whether this is a game fish or not. It is here inserted chiefly because of the danger of mistaking it for a Perch or a small Wall-eyed Pike.

NAMES: Sand Roller. *Color Plate 56.*

DISTRIBUTION: Alberta to Quebec and south to Kansas, Missouri, Kentucky, and Virginia, but not common south of the Great Lakes.

DISTINGUISHING CHARACTERS: A peculiar translucency. Adipose fin. Two spines in the short, median dorsal fin and one spine in the anal. Scales have very fine saw-toothed edges.

SIZE: Six to 8".

FOOD: Crustaceans, insects.

HABITS: Clear cold water; great numbers run into tributary streams to spawn.

Yellow Perch   *Perca flavescens* (Mitchill)

NAMES: Raccoon Perch, American Perch, Red Perch, Ringed Perch, Striped Perch. *Color Plate 56.*

DISTRIBUTION: Hudson Bay drainage of eastern Canada south to Kansas and northern Missouri, Illinois, Indiana, and western Pennsylvania; Nova Scotia to South Carolina. Has been introduced on the Pacific slope.

DISTINGUISHING CHARACTERS: The color pattern. Separate dorsal fins, the spines strong. Profile of head concave above the eyes, making a humped outline before the beginning of the dorsal fin.

SIZE: Averages 1 to 2 pounds; reaches 4.

FOOD: Small water animals, worms, crustaceans, insects, fishes.

HABITS: Quiet streams and ponds, also rivers where there is not a strong current. The larger ones run as deep as 30'.

Wall-eyed Pike   *Stizostedion vitreum* (Mitchill)

NAMES: Pike Perch, Jack Salmon, Blue Pike, Green Pike, Yellow Pike, Yellow Pickerel, Doré, Dory, Pickerel, Walleye, Yellow Pikeperch. *Color Plate 57.*

Distribution: Athabaska Lake, Alberta–Saskatchewan, and Hudson Bay to Labrador; south on Atlantic slope to North Carolina; west of the mountains to Georgia, Alabama, Arkansas, and Nebraska. Common throughout the Great Lakes region.

Color: Occasionally there are indefinite crossbars.

Distinguishing Characters: Strong canine teeth. Upper jaw reaches to beneath the hind margin of eye. Body long and slender. Black blotch on the membrane of the dorsal spines.

Size: Rarely over 10 pounds; averages 2 to 7, but reaches 25.

Food: Fishes, crayfish.

Habits: A fish of clear, moderately deep water. Prefers lakes. Very abundant in Lake Erie.

Sand Pike   *Stizostedion canadense* (Smith)

Names: Sauger, Gray Pike, Ground Pike, Pike Perch, Pickering, Pickerel, Jack, Horsefish, Eastern Sauger. *Color Plate 57.*

Distribution: Hudson Bay drainage to New Brunswick; southward west of the Appalachians to West Virginia, to the Tennessee River in Alabama, and to Arkansas and Iowa; Great Lakes region. Common in Lake Erie.

Distinguishing Characters: Round black spots on the dorsal fin; no black blotch on end of spinous dorsal. Cheeks closely scaled.

Size: One to 2 pounds; not usually more than 1'.

Food: Fishes.

Habits: Silty rivers and large lakes.

BLACK BASSES: Although the finer classification of the Black Basses is still being worked on, the Small-mouth, Large-mouth, and Spotted are scientifically established.

LARGE-MOUTH
BLACK BASS

SMALL-MOUTH
BLACK BASS

TROUTPERCH

PLATE 56

YELLOW PERCH

WALL-EYED PIKE

PLATE 57

SAND PIKE

Small-mouth Black Bass   *Micropterus dolomieu* Lacépède

NAMES: Achigan, Black Bass, Black Perch, Bronze Back, Brown Bass, Gold Bass, Little Bass, Redeye, Swago Bass, Tiger Bass.

DISTRIBUTION: Very wide, due to introduction, and somewhat indefinite, due to misidentifications in the past. Great Lakes; St. Lawrence system; Upper Mississippi, Ohio, and Tennessee River systems; New England to Florida; California to British Columbia. Not present in the Gulf States. *Color Plate 58.*

COLOR: This varies from light to dark, depending on the background.

DISTINGUISHING CHARACTERS: (See figure.) End of upper jawbone does not extend beyond a vertical dropped from the back of the eye. The dorsal fin is not deeply notched as it is in the Large-mouth, and there are no lines of dark dots on the lower half of the sides as in the Spotted Bass. Small scales on the bases of the membranes of the dorsal and anal fins. Cheek scales in 12 or more rows.

SIZE: Averages about 5 pounds or less; 7 to 10 is large; runs to 14.

FOOD: Crayfish, fishes, insects. Apt to feed in early morning near shores.

HABITS: Clear flowing streams and large clear lakes. Not present in sluggish water and not apt to be in trout streams.

Hubbs and Bailey (1940) find a local variety of the Small-mouth, the Neosho Small-mouth (*Micropterus dolomieu velox*), in the Neosho River system and adjacent tributaries of the Arkansas River in Missouri, Oklahoma, and Arkansas.

Spotted Bass   *Micropterus punctulatus* (Rafinesque)

NAMES: Kentucky Bass.

DISTRIBUTION: "Southern Ohio and West Virginia to southern Illinois, southeastern Kansas, eastern and southern Oklahoma, and east-central Texas and east to Alabama, western Georgia, and the Tennessee River drainage of Virginia." (Hubbs and Bailey)

COLOR: Very similar to that of the Large-mouth Black Bass. Dark longitudinal line, and dark lines of spots on lower half of sides. A fairly conspicuous spot on the base of the tail.

DISTINGUISHING CHARACTERS: Small size. Tail spot. Lines of spots. Bases of membranes of dorsal and anal fins scaled. End of upper jawbone not reaching beyond a vertical from hind margin of the eye. Dorsal not deeply notched. Cheek scales usually in 12 or more rows.

SIZE: Maximum 15″, usually less.

FOOD: Crayfish, fishes.

HABITS: In North, sluggish streams; in South, cooler streams with gravel and sand bottoms. Common in the Gulf States.

Hubbs and Bailey (1940) find three subspecies of this—the Alabama Spotted Bass (Alabama River system in Mississippi, Alabama, and Georgia); the Wichita Spotted Bass (Wichita Mountains, Oklahoma), and the Texas Spotted Bass (Colorado, San Antonio, and Guadalupe systems of south-central Texas). I give these because slight variations found in the Spotted Bass in these localities might otherwise lead the angler to think it some other fish.

Large-mouth Black Bass *Huro salmoides* (Lacépède)

NAMES: Straw Bass, Green Bass, Bayou Bass, Slough Bass, Lake Bass, Moss Bass, Grass Bass, Marsh Bass, Oswego Bass, Green Trout. *Color Plate 58.*

DISTRIBUTION: Southern Canada through the Great Lakes system, the Mississippi Valley and to northeastern Mexico and Florida, and north along the coastal plain to North Carolina. Widely introduced elsewhere and extremely numerous in California.

COLOR: The dark dots below middle of sides do not form lengthwise streaks as in the Spotted Bass. The other dark markings shown in the plate vary in intensity and may not be visible at all.

DISTINGUISHING CHARACTERS: Dorsal is so deeply notched as to appear completely divided. No scales on the bases of dorsal and anal membranes. End of upper jawbone reaches slightly beyond back of the eye. Cheek scales usually in 9 to 12 rows.

SIZE: Seldom over 8 pounds in the North; runs larger in Florida; California, 9 or 10 as a maximum.

FOOD: Fishes.

HABITS: Characteristically a fish of warm, sluggish, and muddy water, but often taken in the same waters with the Small-mouth. Abundant in the Gulf States and the Mississippi Valley.

Redeye Bass *Micropterus coosae* Hubbs & Bailey

This is a stream fish from the Alabama and Chattahoochee River systems in Alabama and Georgia, and the Coosa and Savannah River systems in Georgia. There are scales on the dorsal and anal membranes at their bases. The tail lobes are rounded. The upper jawbone does not reach the back of the eye. The outline of the dorsal fin is the same as in the Small-mouth. There are lines of spots on the lower half of the sides, as in the Spotted. There is no tail spot in the adult. There is a black spot on the hind tip of the gill cover.

SMALL-MOUTH BLACK BASS

LARGE-MOUTH BLACK BASS

PLATE 58

SACRAMENTO PERCH

GREEN SUNFISH

PLATE 59

Sacramento Perch   *Archoplites interruptus* (Girard)

DISTRIBUTION: Sacramento-San Joaquin basin and tributary waters. Not abundant. *Color Plate 59.*

COLOR: Varies from almost wholly black to almost wholly silvery; alternating pale and dusky blotches on the sides.

DISTINGUISHING CHARACTERS: Scales saw-toothed on back margin. Dorsal fin outline not deeply notched, and rayed part has a very rounded margin. Color. Spot on gill cover. Rounded corners of the very strongly concave tail margin.

SIZE: One to 2′; usually smaller. This length is very unusual.

THE SUNFISHES comprise a very large group, all rather closely resembling each other; few ever as much as 8″ in length. Difficulty in identification is added to by hybridization, and their ranges are impossible to define clearly because of this and because of very wide introduction.

They are all apt to be seen swimming around in small groups or schools, and they all have the same general body form. They run small but are gamy.

Green Sunfish   *Lepomis cyanellus* Rafinesque

NAMES: Blue-spotted Sunfish, Blackeye Sunfish, Little Redeye, Creek Sunfish, Blue Bass, Blue Sunfish. *Color Plate 59.*

DISTRIBUTION: New Mexico, Colorado, South Dakota, Minnesota, Wisconsin; east to Ontario, western New York; south to Georgia and the Gulf States. Introduced in California.

COLOR: The black gill-cover spot is only on the bony part, not on the membrane in back of it.

DISTINGUISHING CHARACTERS: Light color; gill-cover spot. Short, round pectoral fins; 44 or more scales in the lateral line.

SIZE: Up·to 6″ or 8″ and under 1 pound.

FOOD: Fishes, insects, crayfish.

HABITS: Likes small, sluggish creeks and occurs in small lakes, ponds, and pools.

Bluegill Sunfish   *Lepomis macrochirus* Rafinesque

NAMES: Bluegill, Blue Sunfish, Blue Perch, Red-breasted Sunfish, Blue Bream, Copper-nosed Bream, Dollardee.

DISTRIBUTION: Minnesota, Great Lakes to Lake Champlain; Mississippi River to Florida and Arkansas; north from Florida to New Jersey. Introduced and abundant in California in lakes and ponds of the Sacramento-San Joaquin basin and elsewhere.

DISTINGUISHING CHARACTERS: The color. The bone under the

"ear flap" on the back of the gill cover extends to the margin of the flap, or almost there. *Color Plate 60.*

SIZE: Reaches 12″ to 14″ and a weight of 1½ pounds, but averages less than 1 pound.

FOOD: Insects, fishes, crustaceans.

HABITS: Lakes, ponds, and quiet streams. Our best-known sunfish. In 5′ to 15′ of water, near water plants, moving around in small groups. Frequently found in the same places as the Largemouth Black Bass.

Pumpkinseed   *Eupomotis gibbosus* (Linnaeus)

NAMES: Common Sunfish, Kiver, Kivvy, Pond Perch, Red Belly, Robin, Ruff, Sun Bass, Yellowbelly, Sunny.

DISTRIBUTION: Southern Canada, North Dakota south to the Gulf States, Maritime Provinces south to Florida. Pennsylvania, Ohio, Missouri. Common in Great Lakes region.

COLOR: Varies, with stripes and bars sometimes very conspicuous. *Color Plate 60.*

DISTINGUISHING CHARACTERS: Red spot on gill cover; sometimes bright blue stripes on cheek. Very deep-bodied. Gill cover not flexible behind.

SIZE: Maximum about 8″ and under 1 pound.

FOOD: Insects, crayfish, crustaceans, snails.

HABITS: Weedy parts of ponds and streams. Frequently seen in schools near shores.

Yellowbreast Sunfish   *Lepomis auritus* (Linnaeus)

NAMES: Long-eared Sunfish, Horn-eared Sunfish, Red Sunfish, Red Perch, Robin Perch, Yellowbelly, Tobaccobox, Redbreast, Black-eared Pondfish, Kivver, Leatherear, Robin.

DISTRIBUTION: Maine to Florida and Louisiana; Minnesota east. Most abundant east of the Alleghenies and south of New York.

DISTINGUISHING CHARACTERS: Ear flap is long, narrow, and black; usually has a pale lower edge. *Color Plate 61.*

SIZE: Maximum 8″ and about 1 pound.

FOOD: Fishes, insects, crustaceans.

Long-eared Sunfish   *Lepomis megalotis* (Rafinesque)

NAMES: Big-eared Sunfish, Longear, Black-tailed Sunfish, Long-scaled Sunfish, Red-bellied Bream, Blackears, Red-eyed Sunfish, Tobaccobox. *Color Plate 61.*

DISTRIBUTION: Widely distributed: Mississippi Valley to Minnesota; North Carolina to Florida and the Gulf States. Very abundant in Kentucky.

BLUEGILL SUNFISH

PUMPKINSEED

PLATE 60

YELLOWBREAST SUNFISH

LONG-EARED SUNFISH

PLATE 61

COLOR: Variable; usually brilliant blue and orange with spots and wavy lines. Iris red.

DISTINGUISHING CHARACTERS: Large ear flap with a narrow, pale blue or red margin. Brilliant color.

SIZE: Maximum 8″; averages 3½″ to 6″.

FOOD: Chiefly insects.

HABITS: Large rivers and clear streams.

Stumpknocker *Lepomis punctatus* (Cuvier & Valenciennes)

NAMES: Spotted Sunfish, Spotted Bream, Chinquapin Perch.

DISTRIBUTION: South Carolina to Florida.

COLOR AND DISTINGUISHING CHARACTERS: Numerous small dark bronze specks all over an olive ground color.

Western Shell Cracker *Lepomis microlophus* (Günther)

NAMES: Red-eared Sunfish.

DISTRIBUTION: Mississippi River between Iowa and Illinois; southern Indiana to Alabama and the Rio Grande. Introduced elsewhere.

COLOR: Greenish or blue and green with a broad scarlet margin on the gill cover.

DISTINGUISHING CHARACTERS: Scarlet edge of gill cover.

SIZE: Slightly larger than most of the sunfishes.

HABITS: Bayous, large warm rivers and lakes. Widely known in Florida and the Mississippi Valley.

Warmouth *Chaenobryttus coronarius* (Bartram)

NAMES: Goggle-eye, Bigmouth, Redeye, Sac-à-lait, Indianfish, Sun Trout, Big-mouthed Sunfish, Warmouth Bass.

DISTRIBUTION: Great Lakes to Gulf Coast.

DISTINGUISHING CHARACTERS: Black streaks on base of last few rays of dorsal fin. *Color Plate 62.*

SIZE: Usually under 1 pound; maximum slightly over 2.

FOOD: Fishes, insects.

HABITS: Deep holes, muddy water, weed beds, around bridges.

Rock Bass *Ambloplites rupestris* (Rafinesque)

NAMES: Redeye, Goggle-eye, Rock Sunfish. *Color Plate 62.*

DISTRIBUTION: Manitoba; Great Lakes south, west of the Alleghenies, to the Gulf Coast. Abundant in the Great Lakes and tributary streams and in the small lakes and streams of the Upper Mississippi Valley.

DISTINGUISHING CHARACTERS: Robust body. The dark, uneven markings. Red eye. Six spines in the anal fin.

SIZE: Reaches 1½′ and 2 pounds; averages less.

FOOD: Crayfish, fishes, insect larvae.

HABITS: Prefers clear, rather cool water.

Flier   *Centrarchus macropterus* (Lacépède)

NAMES: Round Sunfish.

DISTRIBUTION: Mississippi Valley to Illinois; Virginia south to the Gulf coast.

COLOR: Greenish, with broken lines of round dark dots; a dark streak below the eye; fins mottled.

SIZE AND HABITS: Abundant in lowland streams, ponds, and bayous. Maximum length 6″.

White Crappie   *Pomoxis annularis* Rafinesque

NAMES: Sac-à-lait, Crappie, White Bass, Strawberry Perch, Papermouth, Suckley Perch, Tinmouth, Chinquapin Perch, Bachelor, Newlight, Campbellite, Lamplighter, and many other very localized names. *Color Plate 63.*

DISTRIBUTION: Great Lakes and Ontario to the Gulf coast. Widely planted.

DISTINGUISHING CHARACTERS: Five to 7 dorsal spines (usually 6). Outline of back a more S-shaped curve than that of the Black Crappie with which it is often confused.

SIZE: One to 2 pounds. Said to reach 3.

FOOD: Insects, crustaceans, fishes.

HABITS: Sluggish ponds or bayous. Warmish water.

Black Crappie   *Pomoxis nigro-maculatus* (LeSueur)

NAMES: Calico Bass, Strawberry Bass, Grass Bass, Crappie, Papermouth, Tinmouth. *Color Plate 63.*

DISTRIBUTION: Southern Canada; Great Lakes to New Jersey and south to Texas. Has been introduced widely elsewhere, including the Pacific coast.

COLOR: Usually darker than the White Crappie and the markings usually more numerous and irregular.

DISTINGUISHING CHARACTERS: Six to 10 spines in the dorsal fin (usually 7 or 8).

SIZE: Often up to 2 pounds and reaches 4.

FOOD: Fishes, crustaceans.

HABITS: Lakes and large streams; rare in larger lakes.

WARMOUTH

ROCK BASS

PLATE 62

BLACK CRAPPIE

WHITE CRAPPIE

PLATE 63

White Bass   *Lepibema chrysops* (Rafinesque)

NAMES: Barfish. *Plate 64.*

DISTRIBUTION: Great Lakes region from St. Lawrence to Manitoba; southern Ontario to New York; south in the Mississippi Valley to Arkansas; eastern Texas.

COLOR: Metallic gold-silver; narrow dark lines of even, close-set spots along the scale rows from gill cover to tail on upper sides. Lower fins and tail with dusky margins.

DISTINGUISHING CHARACTERS: Eleven to 13 anal rays. Projecting lower jaw. Teeth on the base of the tongue. Dorsal spines graduated in height, progressively lower from front to back.

SIZE: Averages 1 to 3 pounds and 1′ long. Reaches over 1½′.

FOOD: Insects, crustaceans, occasionally fishes.

HABITS: Rivers and streams; deep still lakes. Often seen in schools at surface.

White Perch   *Morone americana* (Gmelin)

NAMES: Silver Perch, Sea Perch. *Plate 64.*

DISTRIBUTION: Nova Scotia to South Carolina. This is a fish of both fresh and brackish waters along the Atlantic coast; sometimes becomes landlocked in fresh water.

COLOR: Dark green on back; silvery or light olive below. Often has pale streaks. When landlocked, it runs dark.

DISTINGUISHING CHARACTERS: Dorsal deeply notched between spines and rays but connected by a very low membrane. Small mouth. No dark stripes.

SIZE: Maximum 15″ and 2 or 3 pounds.

FOOD: Crustaceans, insects, sometimes spawn of other fishes.

Yellow Bass   *Morone interrupta* Gill

NAMES: Streaker, Barfish. *Plate 65.*

DISTRIBUTION: Southern Minnesota, Wisconsin, and Iowa south to Texas and Louisiana. Particularly abundant in the Mississippi Valley.

COLOR: Light brassy with 7 conspicuous lines from gill cover to tail base, the lower ones interrupted, being absent or very faint alternately near the head and near the tail.

DISTINGUISHING CHARACTERS: Small mouth; color markings; no teeth on base of tongue. Ten anal rays; dorsal spines not evenly graduated in height.

SIZE: Averages 1 to 2 pounds; reaches 5 pounds.

FOOD: Fishes.

HABITS: A Southern fish, rare in its northern range. Large

WHITE BASS

WHITE PERCH

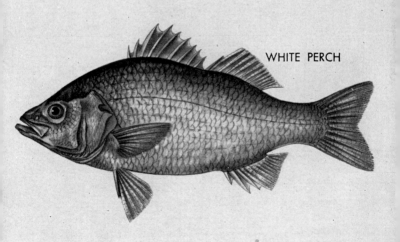

PLATE 64

rivers. In Louisiana in large schools on the shoals of clear waters emptying into the Mississippi.

Rio Grande Perch
Herichthys cyanoguttatus Baird & Girard

This fish looks rather like the Sunfishes but belongs to another family—one very well known to aquarium fanciers, the Cichlids. Within our range it occurs only in Texas. It is frequently encountered in aquaria and grows to a size that can be awkward to keep in the average tank.

COLOR: Grayish-brown, rather light in tone, with numerous small, light blue spots on body, on dorsal fin, and on the rays of the anal fin. A black spot on the middle of the spiny dorsal and another below it on the body; a black spot at the tail base. Dusky vertical bars appear in the breeding season.

DISTINGUISHING CHARACTERS: The only one of the family in our range. Color pattern. Typical Cichlid arrangement of the lateral line which begins, as usual, back of the gill cover toward its top, runs for a short distance, then stops and is continued lower down on the body.

SIZE: Various maximums are given for this fish, but a conservative one would be 6″ to 7″.

Fresh-water Drum   *Aplodinotus grunniens* Rafinesque

A fresh-water member of the Croaker family. *Plate 65.*

NAMES: Sheepshead, Fresh-water Sheepshead, Gaspergou, Crocus, Croaker, Perch, Gray Perch, Thunder Pumper, Bubbler. The name White Perch might well be eliminated for this fish.

DISTRIBUTION: Manitoba and Ontario; Great Lakes; Montana and Nebraska to Pennsylvania and south to the Gulf States.

COLOR: Dusky on the upper part of the body; sides dull silver with rather yellowish or pinkish iridescence, or very dark, rather metallic gray. Sometimes there are dusky oblique streaks along the scale rows of the back.

DISTINGUISHING CHARACTERS: Coarse throat teeth. Continuous dorsal fin; 2 spines in the short anal fin.

SIZE: One of the largest fresh-water fishes, reaching a weight of 60 pounds.

FOOD: Mussels, which it grinds up with its throat teeth; mollusks, crustaceans, and, occasionally, fishes.

HABITS: Produces the peculiar croak of its family. Fond of muddy bottoms and west of the Alleghenies frequents large rivers.

YELLOW BASS

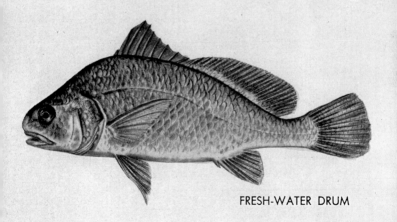

FRESH-WATER DRUM

PLATE 65

THE HERRINGS are a group of marine fishes some of which spawn in fresh water, where they are most often taken by anglers. They are characterized by a single short dorsal fin in the middle of the back and a forked tail fin. No lateral line is visible.

Alewife   *Pomolobus pseudoharengus* (Wilson)

NAMES: Branch Herring, Big-eyed Herring, Wall-eyed Herring, Spring Herring, Sawbelly, Gray Herring, Golden Shad, Skipjack, Bang. *Plate 66.*

DISTRIBUTION: Lake Ontario and Lake Erie; Labrador to Florida.

COLOR: Gray-green or blue-green on back and upper sides; silvery and sometimes very iridescent below. A small dark spot behind the upper angle of the gill cover and vague dark horizontal lines made by minute dark dots on the scales.

DISTINGUISHING CHARACTERS: A keeled and saw-edged belly. No teeth in adults.

SIZE: Under 1 pound. Maximum length about 15″.

FOOD: Small crustaceans.

HABITS: Sometimes becomes landlocked in fresh water. The schools of Alewife run up rivers and brooks to spawn, usually before the Shad run begins.

Other closely related species are often confused with this fish. The Hickory Shad, *Pomolobus mediocris* (Mitchill) (Maine to Florida), has a very projecting lower jaw. The Skipjack or Blue Herring, *Pomolobus chrysochloris* Rafinesque (Mississippi Valley to Gulf of Mexico), usually has teeth. The Glut Herring, *Pomolobus aestivalis* (Mitchill) (Nova Scotia to Florida), looks almost exactly like the Alewife, and about the only distinguishing character is that its body cavity is lined with black.

Shad   *Alosa sapidissima* (Wilson)

NAMES: Common Shad, American Shad, North River Shad, Potomac Shad, Connecticut River Shad, Delaware River Shad, Susquehanna Shad, Atlantic Shad. *Plate 66.*

DISTRIBUTION: Rare in the Great Lakes and confined to the Lake Ontario basin. Atlantic coast from Newfoundland to Florida. Introduced on the Pacific coast and runs from Fort Wrangell, Alaska, to San Diego, California.

COLOR: Bluish or bluish-green above; sides whitish-silver, a dark spot at the shoulder or a row of several dark spots beginning there.

DISTINGUISHING CHARACTERS: No spines in the short, median dorsal fin. Forked tail fin. Upper jaw with a notch into which the tip of the lower jaw fits.

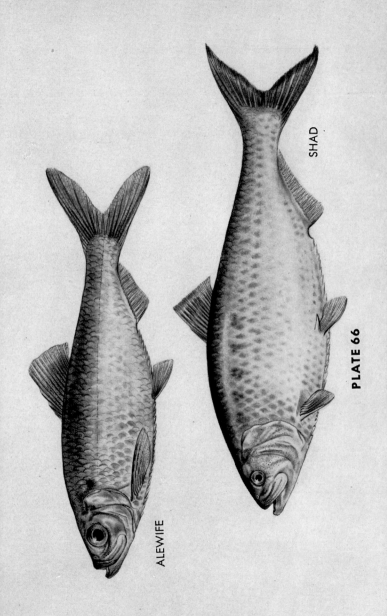

SHAD

PLATE 66

ALEWIFE

SIZE: Reaches 12 pounds in the Atlantic; 14 in the Pacific. Averages about 2½ to 5½.

FOOD: Crustaceans, small fishes, possibly insects.

HABITS: Spends most of its life in the sea but runs up rivers to spawn. The farther northward they are, the later in the year they begin entering rivers.

THE SMELTS include several fishes of the genus *Osmerus,* of which the one below is the best known to anglers. Some have become landlocked in various lakes. There are smelts on the Pacific from San Francisco to Alaska; one runs from Virginia to the Gulf States; another from Maine to New York. For purposes of angling, they all look much alike and are all known as Smelt.

Smelt   *Osmerus mordax* (Mitchill)

DISTRIBUTION: Labrador to New York and the Great Lakes region. *Plate 67.*

COLOR: Greenish above; silvery sided; some tiny dark dots.

DISTINGUISHING CHARACTERS (apply to all the smelts): Adipose fin. One short, spineless dorsal set in the middle of the body. Strong teeth.

SIZE: Averages about 8″ or less; reaches 14″.

FOOD: Crustaceans, insects, fishes.

HABITS: Migrates from salt water into rivers and brackish bay water to spawn and sometimes becomes landlocked. Moves in enormous, closely packed schools.

Eel   *Anguilla bostoniensis* (LeSueur)

DISTRIBUTION: Eastern North America from Labrador south; Mississippi Valley inland to Kansas, Nebraska, Minnesota, Wisconsin, Pennsylvania; the Great Lakes.

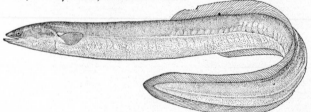

COLOR: When running to sea becomes silvery; otherwise the color varies from yellowish to tan to a dark, almost black, brown.

DISTINGUISHING CHARACTERS: Body form (see figure).

SIZE: Runs from a few inches to a length of 5′ and a weight of 7 pounds, but the maximum is usually about 4 pounds.

SMELT

WHITE SUCKER

PLATE 67

FOOD: Feeds almost entirely at night on any animal food, especially shrimps and crayfish.

HABITS: Spawns in the ocean and dies after spawning. The transparent young work back to coastal waters and enter the mouths of rivers, the females going far inland and sometimes becoming landlocked.

THE SUCKERS: The toothless mouth of the suckers can be protruded to suck in food from the bottom. There are comblike teeth in the throat. The tail is forked. The dorsal fin has no spines. The body is covered with smooth scales, but there are none on the head.

There is no object here in going into detail about the classification of this group, none of which are very gamy although they will take the hook, but some of which are fished for want of anything better.

White Sucker   *Catostomus commersonii* (Lacépède)

NAMES: Black Sucker, Mullet. *Plate 67.*

DISTRIBUTION: Mackenzie River across to the Labrador Peninsula; south on both sides of the Appalachians to Georgia and the Gulf.

COLOR: Varies. May be very dark or fairly light. In the spawning season the males have a black longitudinal band on the side and below it a pinkish one; below that the body is creamy. Otherwise the body is olive.

DISTINGUISHING CHARACTERS: The profile of the snout above the lower lip is vertical. Both lips are thick.

SIZE: To over 20″.

FOOD: Aquatic plants, insects, mollusks, worms.

HABITS: Widely distributed in small and large streams and lakes, occurring generally in clear water, and in spawning season swimming in large schools.

Northern Redhorse   *Moxostoma aureolum* (LeSueur)

NAMES: Redfin, Large-scale Sucker. *Plate 68.*

DISTRIBUTION: Eastern Canada, Montana to Great Lakes-St. Lawrence watershed, south to New York, west to Arkansas and Kansas.

COLOR: Yellowish or light yellowish-pink, becoming paler below. Tail and lower fins red.

DISTINGUISHING CHARACTERS: Bottom margin of lower lip a straight line. Small mouth; short head. Red tail and lower fins.

SIZE: Maximum is 2′ and 8 to 10 pounds.

NORTHERN REDHORSE

CARP

PLATE 68

HABITS: Rivers and lakes, usually in lakes northward in its range. Frequents swiftly moving streams.

Carp   *Cyprinus carpio* Linnaeus

NAMES: German Carp, European Carp. *Plate 68.*

DISTRIBUTION: A European fish widely introduced all over North America both in the East and the West. It has developed many variations in form and color.

COLOR: Very varied. May be yellowish or brassy or silver, very iridescent, or very dark greenish, brown, or almost black.

DISTINGUISHING CHARACTERS: No teeth in the mouth. Teeth in throat. Barbels. A single dorsal fin in the middle. Both dorsal and anal fins have a strong saw-edged spine.

SIZE: Grows to over 3′ and 25 pounds or more. A 70-pound fish has been recorded from Europe.

FOOD: Feeds in the mud on small animals and plants.

HABITS: Prefers quiet water with muddy bottom.

In many localities Carp are considered to have higher nuisance than game qualities.

The following fishes which belong to the same family as the Carp—Cyprinidae—are caught by anglers in some states; in others used only as bait. The ones here included appear to be the only ones ever caught as game, although a few others may be incidentally caught. There are many related genera and species and a good chance of confusion. The use of an up-to-date, technical key is the only sure way of identifying any one of this collection, except the easily recognizable Carp.

Squawfish   *Ptychocheilus oregonensis* (Richardson)

NAMES: Columbia River Squawfish, Chappaul, Yellowbelly, Big-mouth.

DISTRIBUTION: Columbia River basin to Montana and Idaho; north to British Columbia, where it is abundant but not looked upon with much favor as a game fish.

COLOR: Brownish-green on back and sides above; yellowish or silvery below, becoming pale yellowish-white. Some dark spots on the body. In the breeding season the fins are red.

DISTINGUISHING CHARACTERS: Long head, large mouth, no teeth. Single spineless dorsal in the middle of the body.

SIZE: Runs to a length of 4′, but this is not usual.

FOOD: Insects.

HABITS: Lakes and streams. Schools at the surface to feed on insects. Spawns in streams.

SACRAMENTO PIKE

GOLDEN SHINER

PLATE 69

Sacramento Pike   *Ptychocheilus grandis* (Ayres)

NAMES: Sacramento Squawfish. *Plate 69.*

DISTRIBUTION: Rivers of central and northern California and southeastern Oregon.

COLOR: Muddy green with silver on sides. Fins yellowish-red, becoming brighter in the spawning season.

DISTINGUISHING CHARACTERS: As in the Squawfish. Color.

SIZE: Reaches a length of about 4', but this is rare.

FOOD: As in the Squawfish. Eats young trout.

HABITS: In streams; occasionally enters brackish bay water.

Golden Shiner   *Notemigonus crysoleucas* (Mitchill)

NAMES: Eastern Golden Shiner, American Roach, Roach, Shiner, American Bream, Bream, Dace, Bitterhead, Chub, Gudgeon, Windfish. *Plate 69.*

DISTRIBUTION: New Brunswick; St. Lawrence River; eastern part of Lake Ontario basin southward to Florida and Texas.

COLOR: Greenish on the back; pale yellowish-silver on sides. Fins sometimes yellowish-red, sometimes dusky. The fins of the Western Golden Shiner are not red.

DISTINGUISHING CHARACTERS: Belly behind the ventral fins is compressed into a scaleless keel. Single short dorsal with 8 to 10 rays; 5 hooked teeth in the throat.

SIZE: Maximum 1' and about 1½ pounds.

HABITS: Shallow, quiet water and bayous.

In the Lake Ontario basin there is another shiner, the Western Golden Shiner, and in the South Atlantic States there is the Southern Roach. These are all very much alike, and a scientific key would have to be used to distinguish them.

Fallfish   *Semotilus corporalis* (Mitchill)

NAMES: Chub, Silver Chub, Chivin, White Chub, Windfish, Corporal. *Plate 70.*

DISTRIBUTION: Maritime Provinces, northern tributaries of the St. Lawrence River, and the eastern drainage of Lake Ontario, southward, east of the Appalachians, to Virginia. (Hubbs and Lagler.)

COLOR: Steel blue on back; rest of body silver. Fins without markings. Spawning males have red lower fins.

DISTINGUISHING CHARACTERS: Barbel on lower edge of upper jaw. This is very small and often hidden in a groove. About 45 large scales. A few hooked teeth in the throat.

SIZE: Runs to 1½' but may run much smaller in small brooks.

FOOD: Insects, fishes, crayfish, algae.

HABITS: Prefers clear swift streams and clear lakes.

FALLFISH

CUT-LIP MINNOW

PLATE 70

Horned Dace *Semotilus atromaculatus* (Mitchill)

NAMES: Creek Chub, Northern Horned Dace, Northern Creek Chub.

DISTRIBUTION: Montana to the Gaspé Peninsula and south on both sides of the Appalachians to Georgia and the Gulf States; southwest to the Ozark Upland and to the Arkansas and upper Pecos River systems in New Mexico. (Hubbs and Lagler.)

COLOR: Bluish on back; pale, slightly silvery on sides. Not mottled. Black spot at the base of dorsal on the first few rays. This spot in breeding males is bordered with red.

DISTINGUISHING CHARACTERS: Small barbel at end of upper jaw. About 50 to 75 scales. Black spot. Tubercles on head of breeding males.

SIZE: Often very small. Maximum 1'.

FOOD: Algae, insects, crayfish, fishes.

HABITS: Clear creeks; very abundant.

Cut-lip Minnow *Exoglossum maxillingua* (LeSueur)

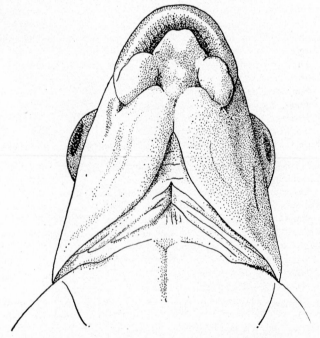

NAMES: Cutlips, Butter Chub, Negro Chub. *Plate 70.*

DISTRIBUTION: Lake Champlain and St. Lawrence River systems and the eastern part of the Lake Ontario watershed including Lake Cayuga, southward east of the Appalachians to the Roanoke River drainage of Virginia. (Hubbs and Lagler.)

COLOR: Olive. No marks on fins. Dusky bar behind the gill cover.

DISTINGUISHING CHARACTERS: Three-lobed lower lip composed of a tongue-shaped bone in the center, flanked by a fleshy lobe on either side. (See figure.) No barbel on upper jaw.

SIZE: 4″ to 8″.

FOOD: Small mollusks, insects.

HABITS: Prefers clear streams with moderate or strong current.

Channel Catfish   *Ictalurus lacustris* (Walbaum)

NAMES: Speckled Catfish, Fiddler, White Cat, Silver Cat.

DISTRIBUTION: Canada (the Prairie Provinces) to the Great Lakes-St. Lawrence basin and Montana to Lake Champlain; southward through the Mississippi Valley to Florida and the Gulf. It is possible that from the Mississippi Valley to the Gulf this species is replaced by another, but for anglers' purposes they are all the Channel Cat. *Plate 71.*

COLOR: Slate gray to silvery; lighter below and usually black-spotted. Albinos have been caught in considerable numbers in Virginia. They are creamy white with pink eyes.

DISTINGUISHING CHARACTERS: Adipose fin not very large. Barbels. Forked tail.

SIZE: Averages 5 pounds; runs to 25 or more.

FOOD: Insects, crayfish, mussels, fishes.

HABITS: Lakes and larger rivers.

Blue Catfish   *Ictalurus furcatus* (Cuvier & Valenciennes)

NAMES: Great Forktail Cat, Mississippi Catfish, Poisson Bleu, Chuckleheaded Cat. *Plate 71.*

DISTRIBUTION: Kansas and Minnesota east through the Ohio Valley and south to the Gulf.

COLOR AND DISTINGUISHING CHARACTERS: Slaty gray or bluish with silvery sides. No spots. Anal fin has 30 to 35 rays. A very large catfish with a forked tail.

SIZE: Averages anywhere up to 20 pounds and runs up to 150.

FOOD: A bottom feeder.

HABITS: Prefers streams and lakes with mud bottoms.

Although accounts of catches of the Blue Catfish are quite often sent in by anglers, it is far more often caught by non-angling methods as a food fish.

CHANNEL CATFISH

BLUE CATFISH

PLATE 71

White Catfish   *Ictalurus catus* (Linnaeus)

NAMES: White Cat of the Potomac, Horned Pout, Fork-tail Catfish. Confusion has been caused because this fish has also been called the Channel Catfish.

DISTRIBUTION: Delaware River south to Texas and successfully introduced into California.

COLOR: Grayish or dull greenish-blue on back and upper sides; silvery below.

DISTINGUISHING CHARACTERS: Its deeply forked tail and its range.

SIZE: Up to 2′.

FOOD: A scavenger, as are the other cats.

HABITS: Rivers and lakes; also brackish water.

Flathead Catfish   *Pilodictis olivaris* (Rafinesque)

NAMES: Mud Catfish, Yellow Cat, Goujon, Morgan Cat, Shovelhead Catfish.

DISTRIBUTION: South Dakota to Michigan; western Pennsylvania; south in the Mississippi Valley to Alabama; Rio Grande and Arkansas.

COLOR: Yellow, mottled with brown.

DISTINGUISHING CHARACTERS: Large adipose fin, nearly as long as the head. Lower jaw strongly projecting. Head very flat on top toward the front. Body slender. Short barbels. Dorsal spine weak; 13 to 16 anal rays. Margin of tail fin slightly rounded (convex).

SIZE: Forty pounds not uncommon and many reported from 50 to 75. Reaches over 100 pounds and 5′.

FOOD: Aquatic animals and smaller fishes.

HABITS: Very abundant in the Lower Mississippi Valley, in large, sluggish rivers.

Black Bullhead   *Ameiurus melas* (Rafinesque)

NAMES: Northern Bullhead, Northern Black Bullhead.

DISTRIBUTION: North Dakota through the Great Lakes region and southern Ontario; northern New York and southward into Tennessee; Kansas, Wyoming, Colorado. *Plate* 72.

COLOR: Greenish-brown to black, shading into greenish or gold. Under part of body as far back as the anal fin is greenish, leaden, or yellowish; never white. Light bar across the base of the tail.

DISTINGUISHING CHARACTERS: Color of under part of body. Light tail-base bar; 17 to 24 anal rays. The barbels below the jaw are dark. No mottling. Flat head; plump body. Tail margin usually pretty straight, sometimes very slightly concave.

SIZE: Smaller than the Brown Bullhead, which it strongly resembles. Averages 6″ to 16″—the latter about the maximum length.

FOOD: Insects, fishes, crayfish.

HABITS: Ponds and sluggish creeks and rivers.

Yellow Bullhead   *Ameiurus natalis* (LeSueur)

DISTRIBUTION: North Dakota through the Great Lakes to New York and south to Texas and Tennessee River system. Although present in the Great Lakes drainage, it seems to be absent in the Lake Superior drainage. There are other subspecies in the Hudson River drainage and coastwise from New Jersey southward. (Hubbs and Lagler, 1941.) *Plate 72.*

COLOR: Yellowish, mottled with darker. Belly bright yellow.

DISTINGUISHING CHARACTERS: Color. Short heavy body and head; wide mouth. Twenty-three to 27 anal rays. Barbels below jaw are pale.

SIZE: Twelve to 18″ or smaller.

FOOD: Insects, crayfish, snails, etc.

HABITS: Sluggish streams and lakes.

Brown Bullhead   *Ameiurus nebulosus* (LeSueur)

NAMES: Speckled Bullhead, Horned Pout, Squaretail Catfish, Black Catfish, Sacramento Catfish, Yellow Catfish. *Plate 73.*

DISTRIBUTION: Southern Canada and North Dakota; Great Lakes region south to the Ohio Valley; New England to Virginia. Another very similar subspecies runs from Illinois and eastern Arkansas to the Carolinas and Florida. Introduced into California and abundant in the Sacramento and San Joaquin rivers, and lakes in central and northern California.

COLOR: Dark brown, blackish, yellowish, or mottled yellowish-green. No pale bar across tail base.

DISTINGUISHING CHARACTERS: Barbels under jaw are dark. No tail bar. Tail square on the margin or rather more deeply concave than in the other bullheads. Seventeen to 24 anal rays. Long body.

SIZE: Averages under 1′, but reaches slightly longer. Maximum 3 or 4 pounds.

FOOD: As of other bullheads.

HABITS: Weedy lakes and sluggish rivers. In California goes into brackish water during the high water of the winter and spring (Walford).

BLACK BULLHEAD

YELLOW BULLHEAD

PLATE 72

Burbot   *Lota maculosa* (LeSueur)

This is a fresh-water member of the Cod family.

NAMES: Ling, Lake Lawyer, Eelpout, Mud Blower, Freshwater Cusk, Gudgeon. *Plate 73.*

DISTRIBUTION: Very widely distributed in central and eastern Canada and in the Mackenzie basin and the Columbia River watershed, also in Wisconsin, Minnesota, Great Lakes basin, and New England. A subspecies in Alaska.

COLOR: Dark olive marbled with black. Sometimes has reddish spots and blotches. Dirty gray underneath.

DISTINGUISHING CHARACTERS: Its shape and the long dorsal and anal fins. A barbel under the chin and a very short one at each front nostril opening. Small imbedded scales.

SIZE: Average weight is 5 pounds, but runs up to 20.

FOOD: Fishes and fish eggs.

HABITS: Deeper waters in large lakes; goes up rivers and creeks to spawn.

One of the fishes whose value to anglers is dependent on the scarcity of other game fishes.

BROWN BULLHEAD

BURBOT

PLATE 73

TABLES

	LBS. OZ.	LENGTH	GIRTH	WHERE	WHEN	ANGLER
Albacore (*Germo alalunga*)	66-4			Catalina, Cal.	1912	Frank Kelly
Amberjack (*Seriola lalandi*)	106	68½"	37"	Pass-a-Grille, Fla.	Mar. 21, 1937	Harvey W. Harker
Barracuda (*Sphyraena barracuda*)	103-4	66"	31¼"	Bahama Islands	1932	Chester E. Benet
Bass, Cal. Black Sea (*Stereolepis gigas*)	515			Catalina, Cal.	1916	Wallace Beery
Bass, Cal. White Sea (*Cynoscion nobilis*)	74-4	76"	30"	Playa del Rey, Cal.	Mar. 8, 1941	W. M. Hartness
Bass, Channel (*Sciaenops ocellatus*)	75-8	64¾"	41"	Cape Hatteras, N. C.	Nov. 29, 1941	Capt. B. R. Ballance
Bass, Sea (*Centropristes striatus*)	8-2			Banks off N. Y.		Peter Volkman
Bass, Striped (*Roccus saxatilis*)	73	60"	30½"	Vineyard Sound, Mass.	Aug. 17, 1913	Chas. B. Church
Blackfish (Tautog) (*Tautoga onitis*)	21-2	30"	21¼"	Sheepshead Bay, N. Y.	Nov. 30, 1937	Albert von Kleist
Bluefish (*Pomatomus saltatrix*)	25			Cohasset Narrows, Mass.	June 16, 1874	L. Hathaway

Species	Weight	Length	Girth	Location	Date	Angler
Bonefish (*Albula vulpes*)	13-12	31"	17"	Bimini, Bahamas	Mar. 9, 1919	B. F. Peek
Cero (Fla. Kingfish) (*Scomberomorus cavalla*)	73-8	62"	32"	Bimini, Bahamas	Feb. 1935	Leonard B. Harrison
Cobia (*Rachycentron canadus*)	102	70"	34"	Cape Charles, Va.	July 3, 1938	J. E. Stansbury
Dolphin (*Coryphaena hippurus*)	67-8	68½"	37½"	Oahu, Hawaii	Aug. 19, 1940	Fred McNamara
Drum, Black (*Pogonias cromis*)	90			Surf City, N. J.	June 21, 1925	Capt. Jack Inman
Flounder, Summer (*Paralichthys dentatus*)	19			Banks off N. Y.	About 1895	Fred Foster
Jewfish (*Promicrops guttatus*)	542			Sarasota, Fla.	May 1923	W. E. Lincoln
Marlin, Blue (*Makaira nigricans ampla*)	737	157"	72"	Bimini, Bahamas	July 16, 1941	J. V. Martin
Marlin, Pacific Black (*Makaira nigricans marlina*)	976	152"	74"	Bay of Islands, N. Z.	Feb. 25, 1926	Capt. Laurie Mitchell
Marlin, Silver (*Makaira nigricans tahitiensis*)	618	138"	62"	Tahiti	Mar. 1930	Zane Grey

CONTINUED ON NEXT PAGE

SALT-WATER RECORDS — ROD-AND-REEL CATCHES

	LBS. OZ.	LENGTH	GIRTH	WHERE	WHEN	ANGLER
Marlin, Striped (*Makaira mitsukurii*)	692	161″		Balboa, Cal.	Aug. 18, 1931	A. Hamann
Marlin, White (*Makaira albida*)	161	104″	33″	Miami, Fla.	Mar. 20, 1938	L. F. Hooper
Robalo (Snook) (*Centropomus undecimalis*)	50-8	55″		Chagres River, C. Z.	Jan. 2, 1944	Capt. J. W. Anderson
Sailfish, Atlantic (*Istiophorus americanus*)	106			Miami Beach, Fla.	1929	Wm. Bonnell
Sailfish, Pacific (*Istiophorus greyi*)	190	122½″	39″	Charles Island, Galapagos	Feb. 9, 1938	E. Tremayne
Sawfish (*Pristis pectinatus*)	736	175″		Galveston, Tex.	Sept. 4, 1938	Gus Pangarakis
Shark, Mako (*Isuropsis mako*)	1000	144″	96½″	Mayor Island, N. Z.	Mar. 14, 1943	B. D. H. Ross
Shark, Porbeagle (*Lamna nasus*)	1009	126″	72″	Egmont Key, Fla.	Mar. 2, 1936	Al. Hack

Shark, Thresher (*Alopias vulpinus*)	922	166"	93"	Bay of Islands, N. Z.	Mar. 21, 1937	W. W. Dowding
Shark, Tiger (*Galeocerdo tigrinus*)	1382	176"	96½"	Sydney Head, Aus.	Feb. 22, 1939	Lyle Bagnard
Shark, White (*Carcharodon carcharias*)	1919		70"	Kangaroo Island, Aus.	May 12, 1941	G. R. Cowell
Swordfish (*Xiphias gladius*)	860	165"		Tocopilla, Chile	Apr. 28, 1940	W. E. S. Tuker
Tarpon (*Tarpon atlanticus*)	247	89½"		Panuco River, Mex.	Mar. 24, 1938	H. W. Sedgwick
Tuna, Allison (*Neothunnus allisoni*)	265	73"	53"	Makua, Hawaii	July 31, 1937	J. W. Harvey
Tuna, Bluefin (*Thunnus thynnus*)	927	123"	80"	Ipswich Bay, Mass.	Aug. 25, 1940	J. Vernaglia
Tuna, Dog-toothed (*Gymnosarda nuda*)	151-8			Tahiti	Feb. 15, 1936	Dr. S. Rabinovitch
Wahoo (*Acanthocybium solandri*)	133-8	83"	31"	Greer Cay, Bahamas	June 15, 1943	K. L. Ames, Jr.
Weakfish (*Cynoscion regalis*)	17-8	46"	19"	Mullica River, N. J.	Sept. 30, 1944	A. Weisbecker, Jr.
Weakfish, Spotted (*Cynoscion nebulosus*)	12-12	35"	16⅛"	Cocoa, Fla.	Mar. 7, 1944	A. W. Rowe
Yellowtail (*Seriola dorsalis*)	88	64"	31"	Bermagui, Aus.	Apr. 23, 1938	Clive Firth

Courtesy of the INTERNATIONAL GAME FISH ASSOCIATION

FRESH-WATER RECORDS

ROD-AND-REEL CATCHES

	LBS. OZ.	LENGTH	GIRTH	WHERE	WHEN	ANGLER
Black Bass, Large-mouth (*Huro salmoides*)	22-4	32½"	28½"	Montgomery Lake, Ga.	June 2, 1932	George W. Perry
Black Bass, Small-mouth (*Micropterus dolomieu*)	14	28"	21¼"	Oakland, Fla.	Feb. 9, 1932	Walter Harden
Carp (*Cyprinus carpio*)	42	42"	29"	Rappahannock River, Va.	May 9, 1930	Robert W. Harris
Catfish, Channel (*Ictalurus lacustris*)	27-4	38"		Lake Ericson, Nebr.	Sept. 16, 1944	Alfred L. Chantry
Muskellunge (*Esox masquinongy*)	62-8	56½"	29¼"	Lake St. Clair, Mich.	June 20, 1940	Percy P. Haver
Perch, White (*Morone americana*)	4-9	20½"	15⅜"	Keokuk, Ia.	June 3, 1935	J. W. Eakins
Perch, Yellow (*Perca flavescens*)	4-3½			Bordentown, N. J.	May 1865	Dr. C. C. Abbot
Pickerel (*Esox niger*)	10-10	36"		MacGregor Lake, Que.	Sept. 2, 1935	G. Scattergood
Pike, Northern (*Esox lucius*)	46-2	52½"	25"	Sacandaga Reservoir, N. Y.	Sept. 15, 1940	Peter Dubuc

Species	Weight	Length	Girth	Location	Date	Angler
Pike, Wall-eyed (*Stizostedion vitreum*)	22-4	36¼"	21"	Fort Erie, Ont.	May 26, 1943	Patrick E. Noon
Salmon, Atlantic (*Salmo salar*)	79-2			Tanaelv, Nor.	1928	Henrik Henriksen
Salmon, Chinook (*Oncorhynchus tschawytscha*)	83			Umpqua River, Ore.	1910	F. R. Steel
Salmon, Landlocked (*Salmo salar sebago*)	22-8	36"		Sebago Lake, Me.	Aug. 1, 1907	Edward Blakely
Trout, Brook (*Salvelinus fontinalis*)	14-8			Nipigon River, Ont.	July 1916	Dr. W. J. Cook
Trout, Brown (*Salmo eriox*)	39-8			Loch Awe, Scot.	1866	W. Muir
Trout, Cut-throat (*Salmo clarkii*)	41	39"		Pyramid Lake, Nev.	Dec. 1925	John Skimmerhorn
Trout, Lake (*Cristivomer namaycush*)	63	47½"		Lake Athapapuskow, Man.	Aug. 22, 1930	Miss L. L. Hayes
Trout, Rainbow or Stlhd. (*Salmo gairdnerii*)	29	40"	24½"	Chehalis River, Wash.	Jan. 6, 1930	E. E. Ames

Courtesy of FIELD AND STREAM *Magazine*

KEY TO GROUPS

BAR-BELS	SCALES	TEETH JAW	TEETH ROOF OF MOUTH	DORSALS SINGLE NO SPINES	DORSALS SINGLE SPINES & RAYS	DORSALS TWO NO SPINES	DORSALS TWO SPINES & RAYS	DORSALS TWO NO SPINES	DORSALS THREE NO SPINES	FINLETS FOLLOW DORSAL & ANAL	LATERAL LINE BONY PLATES	LATERAL LINE	OTHER DISTINGUISHING CHARACTERS	GROUP OR FISH
x	x	x	none		x							x	2 anal spines. Throat teeth.	CROAKERS
x	x	x	none				x					x	2 anal spines. Throat teeth.	CROAKERS
none	x	x	none		x							x	2 anal spines. Throat teeth.	CROAKERS
"	"	"	"		"							"	Front teeth 3-pointed	RUDDERFISHES (Opal-Eye)
"	"	"	"		"							"	Dorsal spines alternately stronger on right and left sides, and . All teeth pointed: . Side teeth blunt (molar):	GRUNTS PORGIES
"	"	"	"		"							"	12 dorsal spines. Front row of teeth conical and pointing backward. Tail margin rounded.	TRIPLETAIL

WRASSES (Tautog)	16 dorsal spines, 2 rows of conical teeth in each jaw. Tail margin straight with rounded corners.
WRASSES (Hogfish)	First three dorsal spines prolonged into streamers.
WRASSES (California Sheepshead)	Large, forward-sloping canine teeth; corners of tail slightly prolonged.
SURF FISHES	Dorsal spines 11 or less. Tail forked.
CROAKERS	
BARRACUDA	Long head and body. Large fierce, uneven teeth.
COD; POLLACK	One barbel (under chin); 2 anals.
HAKE	Second dorsal much longer than first. Slender body. Sharp teeth.
TARPON	Last dorsal ray prolonged in a streamer. Bony (gular) plate on throat. Very large scales.

CONTINUED ON NEXT PAGE

SALT-WATER FISHES

KEY TO GROUPS

BAR-BELS	SCALES	TEETH JAW	TEETH ROOF OF MOUTH	DORSALS SINGLE NO SPINES	DORSALS SINGLE SPINES & RAYS	DORSALS TWO NO SPINES	DORSALS TWO SPINES & RAYS	DORSALS THREE NO SPINES	FINLETS FOLLOW DORSAL & ANAL	LATERAL LINE BONY PLATES	LATERAL LINE	OTHER DISTINGUISHING CHARACTERS	GROUP OR FISH
"	"	"	"	"	·	·	·	·	·	·	"	Dorsal ray not prolonged. Bony plate on throat.	TEN-POUNDER
"	"	"	"	"	·	·	·	·	·	·	"	Dorsal ray not prolonged. No bony plate on throat. Upper jaw overlaps mouth.	BONEFISH
"	"	"	"	"	·	·	·	·	·	·	"	Very high forehead. Very long dorsal. Brilliantly colored.	DOLPHIN
none.	x	x	x	·	x	·	·	·	·	·	x	·	SEA BASSES
"	"	"	"	·	"	·	·	·	·	·	"	Dorsal spines alternately stronger on right and left sides.	SNAPPERS
"	"	"	"	·	"	·	·	·	·	·	"	Dorsal rays completely scaled. Front teeth straight-edged incisors.	RUDDERFISHES

Bony support across cheek, and 5 lateral lines. No anal spines.	GREENLINGS
1 lateral line. No anal spines.	GREENLINGS (Cultus Cod)
3 anal spines.	ROCKFISHES
1 dorsal spine, 19 rays. High forehead.	AFRICAN POMPANO
1 dorsal finlet. 1 anal finlet.	RAINBOW RUNNER
·	MULLET
3 anal spines.	SEA BASSES
2 anal spines.	BLUEFISH
2 anal spines, one free from the fin. Flat head, large mouth.	COBIA
Black lateral line.	SNOOK
·	CALIFORNIA HORSE MACKEREL; JACKS
·	POMPANOS

CONTINUED ON NEXT PAGE

SALT-WATER FISHES

KEY TO GROUPS

BARBELS	SCALES	TEETH JAW	TEETH ROOF OF MOUTH	DORSALS SINGLE NO SPINES	DORSALS SINGLE SPINES & RAYS	DORSALS TWO NO SPINES	DORSALS TWO SPINES & RAYS	DORSALS THREE NO SPINES	FINLETS FOLLOW DORSAL & ANAL	LATERAL LINE BONY PLATES	LATERAL LINE	OTHER DISTINGUISHING CHARACTERS	GROUP OR FISH
none	x	x	x				x		x		x		MACKERELS: TUNAS; ALBACORE; WAHOO; SPANISH MACKEREL
none	x	x	none				x		x		x		BONITO
none	none	x	x		x						x		SCULPIN

SPECIAL GROUPS

Tubercles or denticles instead of scales. Teeth in many series in jaws. Fins covered with leathery skin. More than one gill slit.	SHARKS
Skin with denticles, small prickles, or smooth. Body flat—disklike or triangular. Mouth on underside. Sometimes sharp spines on tail.	RAYS
Upper jaw extended into a broad, flat, heavy blade with strong, wide-spaced, peglike teeth on either edge.	SAWFISH
Upper jaw extended into a long cylindrical spear.	SAILFISH; MARLIN
Upper jaw extended into a long, heavy sword which is flat underneath.	SWORDFISH
Both jaws extended into long, fragile, toothed blades. Body cylindrical.	NEEDLEFISHES
Body flat and disklike. Color and both eyes on one side of the head.	FLATFISHES

BARBELS	SCALES	TEETH		ADIPOSE FIN	DORSALS				LATERAL LINE	OTHER DISTINGUISHING CHARACTERS	GROUP OR FISH
		JAW	ROOF OF MOUTH		SINGLE		TWO				
					NO SPINES	SPINES & RAYS	NO SPINES	SPINES & RAYS			
x··	none	x	none	x	·	x	·	·	x	Single dorsal and single pectoral spine.	CATFISHES
none	x	x	x	x	x	·	·	·	x	Mouth small. Teeth weak in jaws and usually none on tongue.	GRAYLINGS
"	"	"	"	"	"	·	·	·	"	Mouth large. Teeth strong.	TROUTS, SALMONS
none	x	x or none	none	x	x	·	·	·	x	Teeth on tongue. Two flaps of membrane between nostrils.	WHITEFISHES
none	x	none	none	x	x	·	·	·	x	No teeth on tongue. One flap of membrane between nostrils.	PILOT
none	x	x	none	none	·	x	·	·	x	Small dorsal on middle of back.	SMELT
none	x	x	none	x	·	x	·	·	x	2 dorsal spines.	TROUTPERCH

CONTINUED FROM PRECEDING PAGE

FRESH-WATER FISHES   KEY TO GROUPS

BARBELS	SCALES	TEETH JAW	TEETH ROOF OF MOUTH	ADIPOSE FIN	DORSALS SINGLE NO SPINES	DORSALS SINGLE SPINES & RAYS	DORSALS TWO NO SPINES	DORSALS TWO SPINES & RAYS	LATERAL LINE	OTHER DISTINGUISHING CHARACTERS	GROUP OR FISH
x	x	x	x	none			x		x	1st dorsal very short; second very long; both same height whole length. Chin barbel and barbel at each nostril.	BURBOT
x	x	none	none	none		x			x	1 strong, saw-edged spine on dorsal and anal; teeth in throat.	CARP (EUROPEAN)
x	x	none	none	none	x				x	Dorsal on middle of back; throat teeth.	CARPS AND MINNOWS
"	"	"	"	"	"				"	Suctorial mouth.	SUCKERS
none	x	x or none	none	none	x				none		HERRINGS
none	x	x	none	none		x			x	Coarse throat teeth. Dorsal deeply notched.	FRESH-WATER DRUM

none	x .	x .	none .	x .	.	.	.	.	x .	Very large eye.	MOONEYES
"	"	"	"	"	.	.	.	.	"	Long, evenly high dorsal; tail margin round.	BOWFIN
"	"	"	"	.	.	.	.	.	"	Head and body long; uneven, strong teeth; dorsal far back.	PIKES
none	x .	x .	none.	.	x .	.	.	.	. x	. . . . . .	BLACK BASS— SUNFISH GROUP; WHITE PERCH
none	x .	x .	none.	.	.	.	x .	.	. x .	. . . . .	BASSES; PERCHES

SPECIAL GROUP

Dorsal begins well back on body and is continuous with anal, rounding the tail. Snakelike body. Minute scales.. . . . . EEL

INDEX

The first page number refers to the main section in which the fish is discussed.